MICROBIOLOGICAL STANDARDISATION
OF LABORATORY ANIMALS

MICROBIOLOGICAL STANDARDISATION OF LABORATORY ANIMALS

Editor:

F. J. C. ROE, DM(Oxon), DSc(Lond), FRC Path.
Consultant in Toxicology and
Adviser in Experimental Pathology and Cancer Research

Technical Editor:

A. A. DEENY, BSc.

Published by
ELLIS HORWOOD LIMITED
Publishers · Chichester

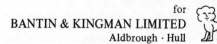

for
BANTIN & KINGMAN LIMITED
Aldbrough · Hull

First published in 1983 by
ELLIS HORWOOD LIMITED
Market Cross House, Cooper Street, Chichester, West Sussex, PO19 1EB, England

The publisher's colophon is reproduced from James Gillison's drawing of the ancient Market Cross, Chichester.

Distributors:

Australia, New Zealand, South-east Asia:
Jacaranda-Wiley Ltd., Jacaranda Press,
JOHN WILEY & SONS INC.,
G.P.O. Box 859, Brisbane, Queensland 40001, Australia

Canada:
JOHN WILEY & SONS CANADA LIMITED
22 Worcester Road, Rexdale, Ontario, Canada.

Europe, Africa:
JOHN WILEY & SONS LIMITED
Baffins Lane, Chichester, West Sussex, England.

North and South America and the rest of the world:
Halsted Press: a division of
JOHN WILEY & SONS
605 Third Avenue, New York, N.Y. 10016, U.S.A.

© 1983 Bantin and Kingman Ltd./Ellis Horwood Ltd.

British Library Cataloguing in Publication Data
Roe, F.J.C.
Microbiological standardisation of laboratory animals.
1. Laboratory animals — Microbiology
I. Title
636.08'85   SF406

ISBN 0-85312-556-2 (Ellis Horwood Ltd., Publishers)
ISBN 0-470-27401-8 (Halsted Press)

Typeset in Press Roman by Ellis Horwood Ltd.
Printed in Great Britain by Unwin Brothers of Woking.

Table of Contents

Foreword

The use of laboratory animals in research is an emotive subject. The response of scientists has been two fold; on the one hand to explore new possibilities for experimental models and on the other to further increase knowledge of the animals and of the techniques used in fields where substitution is both difficult and unrealistic.

The object of the symposium, held by Bantin & Kingman Ltd., in December 1981, upon which this book is based, was for scientists engaged in different branches of medical research to pool their existing knowledge of laboratory animals. It was hoped that researchers would learn more about the condition of animals supplied to them, either from commercial sources or their own animal breeding units.

Standardisation of the microbiology of the laboratory animal is of prime importance, both in terms of reducing variables, which may interfere with the experiment, and ultimately minimising the number of animals used.

As described in the following chapters, the influences of bacteria, viruses and parasites, whether they are pathogenic or not, may have a profound effect on experimental results. The selection of a suitable model based on health criteria is not a new concept. For many years the Medical Research Council Laboratory Animals Centre (LAC) has been grading animals for suppliers on the basis of presence or absence of pathogenic organisms. More recently, many workers have been advocating a more rigorous selection regime where more consideration is given to organisms which may be present, but which do not necessarily result in clinical disease. This presents the research worker with a problem as to how far influences due to these organisms should be considered in the design of the experiments.

Inbred strains of animals are now widely used throughout medical science as their particular characteristics provide a useful tool in pathology, immunology, toxicology, microbiology and oncology.

As a result new methods have had to be developed to monitor the authenticity of each strain. There are sometimes difficulties in equating results from experiments using inbred animals with human conditions. It is hoped that this book will in some way make the choice between inbred or outbred easier.

The main purpose of the book is to present the scientists' view on selection of laboratory animals. The animal has so far escaped the scrutiny that has been the hallmark of controlled experimentation. However, it has become possible with strict microbiological monitoring of animals, with inbred strains, with isolator techniques and many other facilities at the breeders' disposal to provide a more defined experimental model that, in the absence of other viable alternatives takes into account and reduces the variables introduced into an experiment by laboratory animals.

G. C. Bantin,
Managing Director
Bantin & Kingman Ltd.
The Field Station
Grimston
Aldbrough
Hull HU11 4QE

1

The needs of the Toxicologist

G. J. Turnbull, BSc, PhD, Head of Toxicology Department, FBC Limited, Chesterford Park Research Station, Saffron Walden, Essex, CB10 1XL

INTRODUCTION

In this paper I present an industrial toxicologist's view on the need for microbiological standardisation of laboratory animals. Rather than present a catalogue of microbially caused diseases in laboratory animals, which would be the systematic approach, I propose to examine the system; in other words, what a toxicologist does that requires the use of animals of defined microbiological status. By means of a few examples of microbial causes of ill-health in laboratory animals, I will identify the needs of a toxicologist and propose a general pragmatic policy in relation to overt health of animals.

THE TOXICOLOGIST'S USE OF ANIMALS

Toxicity studies are performed to identify toxic properties of a chemical, then quantify that toxicity in terms of dose response (Fig. 1). The experimental toxicologist therefore sets out to produce data on toxicity. The ultimate objective of the toxicologist is to identify the toxic hazard associated with a particular exposure to a chemical. Precautions, that limit the exposure to a chemical, mean that an acceptable level of safety is attained.

Safety is the absence of an unacceptable level of known harm, allowing for planned, and unplanned, events and their likely consequences (Fig. 2). Since people come into contact with chemicals deliberately, by taking a medicine, for instance, and unintentionally when using chemicals, for instance in a factory, I am concerned about the consequences of events involving chemicals in certain environments.

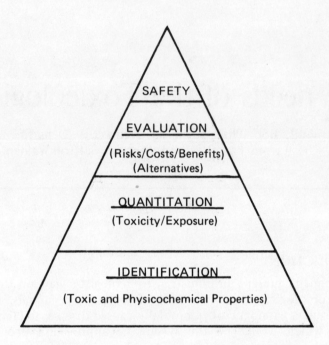

Fig. 1 – Purposes for which the toxicologist uses animals.

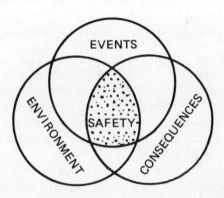

Fig. 2 – What is safety?

As an industrial toxicologist my concern is the safety of chemicals during manufacture and use. The commodities I want before I can consider the safety of a chemical are information, and confidence in that information. The means to obtain some of that information is a model involving a laboratory animal.

Other scientists also use animals as models in their research. Some of my comments could apply to a pharmacologist, for instance, screening novel compounds for possible therapeutic activity. Having said that, safety is an important issue, with ethical implications, and so I want to have particularly clear expectations for my animal model in toxicity testing. I want to be able to interpret animal toxicity data so as to decide the significance of the toxic response and the relevance of the information to man or the target species in question. That target species is not always man.

The animal model provides reproducible circumstances in which toxicologists study the activity of the chemical, commonly at various dose levels, under controlled environmental conditions. These controlled environmental conditions are intended to make the studies reproducible, and allow comparisons to be made between studies. The animal model may be intended for one of several classes of purpose: screening, interim, i.e. to be superseded, definitive.

Fig. 3 shows some of the important variables a toxicologist controls in a study: Duration, Aspect, Route, Model. Screening, or preliminary studies, include the first acute studies on a chemical, and tests to find the dose levels for reproduction and longer term toxicity tests. An example of an interim study is a 90-day dietary study in the rat which will be superseded, if the compound is to be developed as a drug or pesticide, by a chronic study with dosing in excess of two

DURATION:	ACUTE/SUBACUTE/CHRONIC
ASPECT:	GENERAL TOXICITY/REPRODUCTIVE TOXICITY/CARCINOGENICITY/LOCAL OR SYSTEMIC TOXICITY
ROUTE:	ORAL/INHALATION/DERMAL/PARENTERAL
MODEL:	SPECIES, STRAIN, HEALTH STATUS, PROCEDURE, ENVIRONMENT
DOSE:	DAILY RATE/TOTAL

Fig. 3 – Some controlled variables in toxicity tests.

years. This two-year study would be definitive for cumulative toxicity and the ability of the chemical to cause cancer.

The protocols for the experiments by which chemicals are tested for the various aspects of toxicity, such as teratology or local effects on the skin, are by now well established. I am certainly not saying that there is only one correct method for each type of test, only that the experience of many laboratories around the world has resulted in commonly used effective protocols. These protocols the toxicologists adapt to their immediate needs. By now the protocols are tried and tested because they have been validated by testing positive controls, that is chemicals known to produce the particular toxicological effect. Knowing the sensitivity of the various tests the toxicologist then extrapolates from the animal model to man.

THE VALIDITY OF THE ANIMAL MODEL

Knowing that the purpose of the model is to produce information forming the basis for certain decisions on safety, what are the implications of the model failing; that is, failing to give any result at all and needing to be repeated, or failing by showing false negative or positive results? (Fig. 4).

What impact would false negative information have? Could a treatment-related change be obscured by a poorly controlled variable

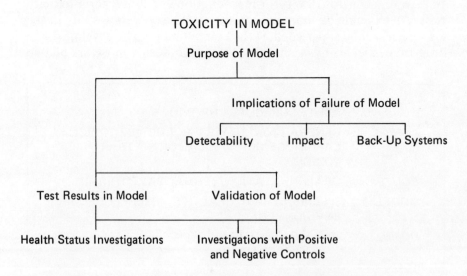

Fig. 4 – The validity of the model.

in a toxicity study, and would this false negative information alone lead to false presumption of safety? False presumption of safety would, of course, be a very serious mistake.

Would a false positive result be detected by the toxicologist; in other words, could disease be mistaken for the consequence of chemical treatment? This false presumption of toxicity might lead to the rejection of a perfectly safe product.

The detectability and impact of failure of the animal model in toxicity testing varies from study to study. There may be back-up systems, or rather the system of toxicity testing may provide a back-up. For instance, acute toxicity is studied in several species, so an inconsistent finding will be highlighted and the work may be repeated. However, there may not be corroborative data for definitive studies such as teratology or carcinogenicity.

The effect of a disease on a toxicity study may be to mask or exacerbate toxicity; alternatively, the toxicity of the compound may exacerbate the disease, perhaps leading to apparently healthy animals becoming unacceptable as animal models.

The studies that validated the use of the model, and the results with concurrent control compounds, help reveal the effects on the animal model of uncontrolled variables, including disease (Fig. 4). Put it this way: the same chemicals have been tested in enough laboratories in animals of different microbiological status to show the variability of the model. You could say that the toxicologist's favourite protocols are the ones that are not greatly sensitive to variations in the microbiological status of the animals.

AVOIDING VARIABILITY IN RESPONSE DUE TO VARIATION IN MICRIOBIOLOGICAL STATUS

Specific investigations are included in a programme of toxicity tests to examine the health status of the animal model (Fig. 5). These health status investigations can be more, or less, invasive, and this determines how often they can be made. For instance, pathological examination clearly calls for killing some animals. This can be additional to the ones about to go on test, or it can be the animals that are part of the toxicity test. In either case the pathologist is looking for changes that are diagnostic of certain disease states. Without killing the animals samples of blood and urine can be taken. The haematological, serum chemistry, and urinalysis profiles may reveal characteristic changes; for instance, characteristic of liver damage. The toxicologist must then decide if this damage is due to disease or is a toxic effect of the chemical being tested.

EXAMINATION FOR ECTOPARASITES AND ENDOPARASITES
PATHOLOGY (GROSS AND MICROSCOPIC)
HAEMATOLOGICAL AND CLINICAL CHEMISTRY PROFILE
EXAMINATION FOR PATHOGEN PROFILE
CONCURRENT USER EXPERIENCE

Fig. 5 – Health status investigations in toxicity testing.

It is customary to examine the pathogen profile, especially in rodents, in order to identify possible causes of disease in the future. Hence the rats that are used for toxicity tests are small samples of the large population that is subject to microbiological monitoring. The toxicologist needs to know the nature of the monitoring and how effective the monitoring is in helping the breeder supply healthy animals.

The experience of users of the supply of animals indicates the actual effect of that microbiological burden under the various husbandry conditions at various times. That experience is the reality of animal health compared with the theoretical indication from microbiological monitoring. Therefore the experience of other UK toxicology laboratories is important to me when I decide on my supply of animals.

In my own laboratory the health status investigations are linked in with the toxicity tests going on. Routinely there are clinical examinations and observations of haematology, clinical chemistry, and pathology. There is also some microbiological surveillance. However, for large laboratories I can see the need for a more intensive integrated approach with regular sampling and reporting that is not tied in with the specific toxicity tests. The extent of health status investigations, and their frequency, depends upon the nature of the work programme. In other words, we are back to the question of the likely impact of a breakdown in animal health and failure of the animal model.

Given certain environmental conditions, a microbial challenge to the animals will result in a disease state that will be recognisable to a greater, or lesser, extent. The purpose of monitoring in relation to toxicity testing is therefore to detect such deteriorations in health. Then a decision can be made whether to accept the animals for use in a study or reject them. Even if a study has started, then monitoring may show disease developing, and there is then the option of terminating the study. The practical criteria for accepting, or rejecting, animals for a study relate to the detectability of disease. Concentrating on microbial causes of disease, detection may be a question of microbiological surveillance, or it may be the effects of infection that are detected.

THE IMPACT OF INFECTIOUS DISEASE DEPENDS ON THE ORGANISM CONCERNED

To illustrate this I will refer to three microbially caused conditions of ill-health in laboratory animals: Tyzzer's disease, chronic respiratory disease (CRD), and sialodacryoadenitis (SDA). In each case I will concentrate on the aetiology, manifestations, and particular problems of control of transmission. These examples illustrate a range of causative organisms, with spore-forming and vegetative phases, and various clinical responses. They will serve to show the impact of animal health on toxicity studies. They show the needs of the toxicologist for a microbiologically standardised supply of animals to match the quality of environment in which they are housed.

Tyzzer's disease (Fig. 6) is fatal in its acute form, and the organism concerned is spore-forming.

Chronic respiratory disease (CRD) (Fig. 7) has a mixed aetiology, a characteristic pulmonary pathology, and it clinically produces a decline in condition.

BACILLUS PILIFORMIS (SPORE FORMING)

CONTAGIOUS

ACUTE, FATAL

PRIMARY INFECTION OF SMALL INTESTINE, WITH FOCAL NECROSIS

BACTEREMIC EMBOLISATION TO MYOCARDIUM WITH MYOCARDITIS

SWOLLEN MESENTERIC LYMPH NODES. FOCAL HEPATIC NECROSIS

Based on Baker *et al.* (1979)

Fig. 6 – Mouse/rat – Tyzzer's Disease.

PASTEURELLA PNEUMOTROPICA/MYCOPLASMA PULMONIS/
?VIRUS

CHRONIC (CARRIER STATUS), PROGRESSIVE
PULMONARY   — MAJOR AIRWAYS CUFFED WITH
                      LYMPHOCYTES, INFILTRATION AND
                      DESTRUCTION OF EPITHELIUM, ACTIVE
                      GERMINAL CENTRES IN CUFFING
               — PERIPHERAL SMALL AIRWAYS AND BLOOD
                      VESSELS WITH LYMPHOCYTE CUFFING,
                      OEDEMA
               — PNEUMONITIS

CLINICAL SIGNS   — CLINICAL DECLINE ESPECIALLY IN OLD
                      ANIMALS, LYMPHOCYTE PROLIFERATION

Based on Lamb, D. (1975)

Fig. 7 – Rat – Chronic Respiratory Disease.

Sialodacryoadenitis (SDA) (Fig. 8) is highly contagious and in the acute form affects the salivary and lacrimal glands. The eyes may be affected and body weight gain may be reversed.

Let us turn now to how such causes of ill-health affect toxicity testing in its various forms. This is where I admit to a strongly pragmatic approach.

Microbiologically — standardise as far as practicable.
Monitor   — for health, not only for microbiological status.
Studies   — terminate, extend, or repeat if necessary.
Plan   — schedule with some provision for contingency.

In relation to the examples I have shown of microbial causes of ill-health how does this approach work?

HIGHLY CONTAGIOUS, NO CARRIER STATUS

SUBCLINICAL ENDEMIC/EXPLOSIVE CLINICAL OUTBREAKS

ACUTE, NON-FATAL:
               SALIVARY AND LACRIMAL GLAND INFLAMMATION,
               NECROSIS, OEDEMA AND METAPLASIA: KERATO-
               CONJUNCTIVITIS, SNEEZING, PHOTOPHOBIA, NASAL
               AND OCULAR DISCHARGE, BODYWEIGHT GAIN
               TEMPORARILY REVERSED

Based on Baker *et al.* (1979)

Fig. 8 – Rat – Sialodacryoadenitis (RNA virus).

Tyzzer's disease

In the case of manifest Tyzzer's disease there is no choice: the overtly affected animals are self-evidently not fit for a toxicity study of any duration. All efforts are then directed at cleaning up and preparing to start over again with a new stock of animals. If that means changing to another breeding supply or even another strain, then the appropriate preliminary toxicity testing may need to be repeated. For instance it may be necessary to establish dose levels of chemical given in the diet ready for a chronic toxicity study by repeating part of the 90-day dietary toxicity study. This would ensure that the new supply of animals was as susceptible to the toxic effects as the original supply. Failure to do this could well mean that the chemical produced excessive toxicity, or no toxic response. In either case the data may be insufficient to decide safety.

If I suspected a subclinical infection with Tyzzer's disease, then, fearing an epidemic outbreak, I would quarantine and probably stop the study. Perhaps ignorance is bliss — how often have animals with a subclinical latent infection been used in studies and not been stressed or subject to an environment that favours expression of the infection?

To draw a general conclusion, any microbiological cause of ill-health as contagious and severe as *Bacillus piliformis* I would treat in the same way.

Chronic respiratory disease (CRD)

CRD is a more elaborate problem. Microbiological status of the breeding colony and the animals received for a particular study only indicate the likely health of animals initially. Histopathological examination of newly received animals certainly helps, but infection and expression of the disease may occur during the toxicity study. Animals that show gross signs of CRD at a few weeks of age are not suitable for any toxicity test, and so I would reject them and start over again with fresh stock rather than take a chance. Certainly for chronic studies, including multigeneration studies, what I want is confidence that the animals started the study with a minimal microbiological burden in relation to CRD.

The key point is to decide what constitutes normal lung pathology, acceptable minor signs of CRD, unacceptable evident CRD, and totally unacceptable gross CRD.

With normal lung parenchyma in rats, there is no inflammatory cell infiltration, and peribronchiolar lymphoid aggregations do not have evident germinal centres. Animals like this would be welcome in any toxicity test.

However, if the screening showed a significant incidence of moderate or severe peribronchial and peribronchiolar lymphoid aggregations, especially with the appearance of germinal centres, then such animals would not be suitable for an inhalation toxicity study or a long-term study. The decision would depend upon both the degree (severity and extent) and the incidence of the finding. In other words how many animals in the sample had such changes, to what severity and to what extent the airways were involved.

If there are perivascular lymphoid aggregations as well as some infiltration of the alveoli at the end of a 90-day study, this finding would not be encouraging, and in animals about to go on a chronic study would be quite unacceptable.

Frequent areas of frank pneumonitis would render the animals unsuited for starting any toxicity test. If large areas of the lung were involved then I doubt if there would be normal respiratory function although the animals could well survive.

Looking higher up the respiratory tract, there may be chronic respiratory disease involving the larynx and trachea. For instance, epithelial and subepithelial inflammatory cell infiltration with associated epithelial hyperplasion would make rats a disaster for use in any inhalation study. In fact I would not want that in many rats in any toxicity test. The message is look at the whole respiratory tract, not just the lung tissue.

The acceptability of minor signs of CRD depends upon the age of the animals, and the intended duration of the study. In a nutshell, what can be accepted at the end of a life-time study probably is not satisfactory at the very start of such a study because of the risk of progression and premature death.

A toxicity study can be scientifically invalid if there is excessive early mortality. For instance, rats treated with a chemical must live to a reasonable age before it can be concluded that the chemical did not cause cancer in them. If the rats died young from respiratory disease that is not possible. Not that survival is the only parameter that overt CRD may affect. Because of possible change in the immune status associated with CRD there may perhaps be other effects.

In general, my planning is directed at minimising the risk of introducing, spreading, or exacerbating CRD. As a contingency, I might plan to totally empty and clean up a building housing subchronic or chronic studies on a periodic basis unless the animals were still clean histologically at the end of tests.

I admit this is a belt and braces approach, but the stakes are so high when it comes to the good survival of animals in a chronic study; the end justifies the means. The same approach applies to inhalation studies, especially those involving repeated exposure where it is very important that respiratory tract disease does not obscure the local toxic effects of the chemical.

As a general conclusion, CRD or a microbiological problem of similar magnitude, I respond to on a case by case basis. The criteria for accepting animals, or prematurely terminating a study, are directed at ensuring adequate survival of the animals and being able to interpret the data on toxicity of the chemical at the end of the study. Toxicity studies are very expensive, especially chronic studies which now cost £¼m each, and so the importance of adequate survival and quality of toxicity data cannot be overstated. There is simply no point in producing toxicity data that cannot be interpreted to elucidate the safety of the chemical that was tested.

Sialodacryoadenitis (SDA)

In the case of SDA, I probably would not even know if there was a subclinical occurrence. If an acute outbreak happens during a short-duration study, for instance an acute test, I would probably terminate the test and repeat the work after a suitable clean-up of the animal rooms and the rest of the facility, and a short quarantine period. If it happened during a reproduction study my reaction would depend on the type of study and the stage of the study. The work of Utsumi *et al.* (1980) showed a lowering of the littering rate when mating coincided with the symptoms of SDA. However, after mating has occurred SDA has much less effect on littering performance. Personal communication from David Cozens at Huntingdon Research Centre is that one to four weeks after the symptoms of SDA the rats reach a normal littering rate. Hence, SDA occurring very early in a teratology study would lead me to terminate the test. If it happened part way through a multigeneration study I would continue the test, but perhaps delaying mating a couple of weeks.

If SDA happened during a 90-day study I would probably continue with the study but might have to repeat or delay the interim clinical studies, or if it happened at the end I might extend the dosing period to allow body weight, clinical laboratory studies, and histopathology (and perhaps relative organ weights) to stabilise.

Fig. 9 shows the affect on body weight in the control groups in three different studies in rats which suffered from an outbreak of SDA at study weeks 2, 10, and 21 respectively. Body weight gain was unaffected in rats only a few weeks old. At week 10 in the study there was 3% loss in body weight in males but almost no loss of weight in females.

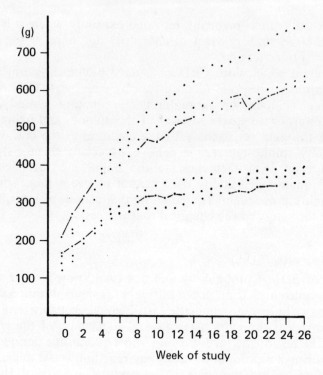

Fig. 9 – Effect of SDA on body growth in untreated control rats in three separate
studies. The effect varies with age.

At study week 21 the loss in body weight was higher, at 6% in
males and 4% in females. Hence the affect on body weight appears
on this limited information to be age-related but relatively limited
and fully reversible.

In the event of an outbreak of SDA one thing I would consider,
depending upon the studies involved, is specifically examining the
eyes for corneal scars after the animals had clinically recovered. This
is because the keratoconjunctivitis can, under certain circumstances,
leave a residual lesion that might decrease the effectiveness of
subsequent eye examinations intended to detect chemically induced
changes. Probably only a few animals would be affected, and this I
would accept rather than terminate the test prematurely.

RECAPITULATION

To sum up, as an industrial toxicologist I employ animal models to
obtain information needed to ensure the safety of people and the

environment. I may be cost-conscious, but then who isn't; yet I will go to very great lengths to protect the investment I make in the animal studies, particularly the chronic tests. The cost of animals is only a small part of my operating cost, but I give a lot of added value to the animals during my studies.

I have a programme of tests to conduct to give information on safety for predetermined dates in a development programme. Those dates commonly cause problems! For instance, I want information on a new pesticide formulation before the climatic seasons bring the first use of that formulation. Hence, I adopt a very pragmatic approach to animal health. My efforts are directed at monitoring the overall health of animals as much as at knowing microbiological status. To apply this pragmatic policy I build some flexibility into my programme so that animals with suspect health status can be rejected from test. In practice, rejecting animals does not happen very often, and that indicates the generally good performance of breeders of laboratory animals.

There is one question I would like to impart to both suppliers and users of animals. What business do you think you are in, and what business are you actually in? What sort of customer do you think you are, and what are you actually buying? As a toxicologist I am a different customer according to the nature of my studies. For chronic studies, which are a huge cash investment, I actually want to purchase information and confidence as much as animals. If the animals start a chronic study with a reasonable microbiological burden, and if my husbandry is up to standard, I should get reasonable survival and a satisfactory study. In this case, what I want from the breeder is assurance that the breeding colony was fairly recently re-derived and is screened microbiologically. Essentially, I want to know that at the time I obtained my animals the colony was in excellent health. As a side comment, I need to be confident that the breeder has retained records of the type of food the animals were given and the environmental conditions. These records are a desirable contribution to the compliance of a toxicity study to codes of Good Laboratory Practice.

Once I have the animals I can monitor the animals as I use them and interpret the results in relation to animal health. The performance of the breeder and, probably more important, my own animal facility can then be decided and improvements made if necessary.

As a toxicologist I need the suppliers of animals to respond positively to me as to each type of customer. In other words, sometimes a customer wants animals, other times he wants animals plus a lot of supportive information.

If there is a problem with animal health I expect the supplier to be active and work with me to identify the cause. I do not accept that the adage of 'buyer beware' applies to animals any more than it applies to less perishable commodities. The goods provided should be adequate for the intended use. Equally, I should take reasonable care of the animals. My failure to provide the necessary environment is the likely cause of many problems of animal health. However, the breeder probably has both the experience and the resources to identify the problem while I may not. The breeder also has a good reputation to protect.

For my part, I should maintain closer contact with the breeders than I do, but to them I am a small client compared with animal users operating screens, for instance, for pharmaceuticals.

On the other hand I maintain contact with other toxicologists using animals to share concurrent user experience on survival and diagnostic pathology. I know I should put more effort into doing this, but the mechanism is lacking.

I suggest that there is a need for the toxicology laboratories and the animal suppliers to develop ways to exchange information much more effectively.

Finally, let me share a toxicologist's nightmare with you. It is an outbreak of a novel form of ill-health during an important study, the results of which are especially wanted by a particular date. Tyzzer's disease in rodents, enteritis in guinea pigs, pulmonary disease in rabbits, and parvovirus in dogs have at various times caused a lot of worry to toxicologists trying to schedule quality studies.

What I want to avoid, above all, is one of my studies being the centre of the next catastrophe for animal health that ruins studies and takes a lot of time and effort to resolve. These things can happen. In the case of oral papilloma in dogs there is benign proliferation of the epithelium. These papilloma occur on the buccal mucosa, and several may be present in each affected animal. There is a viral aetiology to this lesion, but when many of a batch of dogs showed the same condition it could have caused my laboratory problems in interpreting the findings in the study.

Likewise, in my laboratory, polyarteritis in 8 out of 32 dogs certainly complicated the interpretation of clinical data, although the pathology was clearly unrelated to treatment with chemical. This degenerative condition of vessels occurred in several tissues.

Similarly in rats, the haematology consistently showed a relatively high white cell count when animals were housed in one building. In a concurrent group, in another building on the same site, the same batch of animals appeared totally normal, yet the husbandry conditions were conventional rather than barrier. Was it some latent subclinical infection perhaps being unmasked by stress to animals in one building only? I do not know and may never know.

But let me ask you, can you predict where the next major health breakdown will take place or what will be the cause, or how it will be detected?

REFERENCES

Baker, J. H., Lindsey, J. R. & Weisbroth, S. H. (1979) Editors. *The laboratory rat*. Academic Press, London.

Lamb, D. (1975). *Lab. An.,* **9**, 1-8.

Utsumi, K., Ishikawa, T., Maeda, T., Shimuzu, S., Tatsumi, H. & Fujiwara, K. (1980) *Lab. An.,* **14**, 303-307.

2

The needs of the Pathologist

D. A. Rutty, Safety of Medicines Dept., Imperial Chemical Industries Ltd., Pharmaceuticals Division, Alderley Park, Macclesfield SK10 4TG

INTRODUCTION

I am concerned with the safety evaluation of new medicines emerging from the research programme of ICI's Pharmaceutical Division. In this role I need to consider the quality of the laboratory animal and its influence on the experiment fairly widely and not only from the viewpoint of microbiological problems. Dr Turnbull has just given an excellent background description of the toxicologists task in testing pesticides, and much of what he has said about his work and problems also applies to the testing of new medicine. The ultimate test of any new medicine is, of course, its efficacy and safety in man. It is clearly unethical to obtain such information directly from patients or volunteers without first gathering pertinent information in the laboratory. What we do is to obtain safeguards in the laboratory by means of modelling. The models we use may be *in vitro, ex vivo*, or *in vivo*.

It is an obvious truth that the conclusions to be drawn from animal experiments are only as good as the experimental design and the quality of the data produced. It follows that it is of crucial importance to use a species, strain, and source of animal that is appropriate for the purpose intended, i.e. a correct and reliable experimental model.

Let me start with an example – a worm called *Trichosomoides crassicauda* which lives in the urinary tract of the rat. It causes hyperplasia of the transitional epithelium; it either gives the erroneous impression of tumour formation or it may act in concert with carcinogenic chemicals to raise the tumour yield. It may do this either by virtue of its own irritancy or by the vesicular calculi it provokes and/or by increasing bladder tissue exposure to the chemical.

Another quite different example is that presented by a protozoon *Nosema cuniculi*, an encephalitozoon which affects the rabbit brain. This protozoon may be latent as an infection, and yet seriously disrupt pyrogen tests which depend upon a very stable body temperature prior to challenge with a test substance.

I also met it when working in a virus-testing area where rabbits were used for providing kidney cell cultures and were also inoculated with viral agents. It was a great nuisance because the organism may not always be demonstrated in the CNS lesions, thus complicating diagnosis. The kidney may be affected with radial streaks of parenchymal degeneration and inflammation. At high power, parasites may be seen in a microcyst (Fig. 1).

These were two specific problems affecting specific test systems. It has been suggested by others that a single health status could suit all purposes. I do not believe this is true, e.g. a type of animal status suitable for transplanting tumours could be quite unsuited for studying enteric metabolism of xenobiotics.

Considerable effort has been made to 'standardise' the laboratory animal and reduce variability within experiments. Regardless of the imprecision of the term specific pathogen free (SPF), we know that

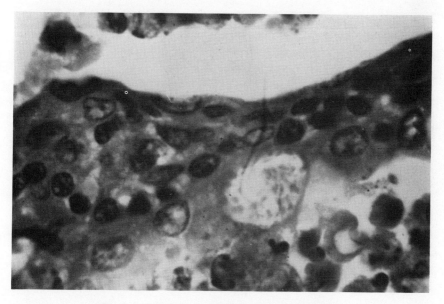

Fig. 1 – *Nosema cuniculi* infection in rabbit kidney.

the approach has improved the quality of animals enormously; so much so that it is now increasingly difficult to obtain specimens of certain once very common rodent diseases.

One of the major benefits of SPF rodents was the elimination of the agents causing chronic respiratory disease, such as *Mycoplasma pulmonis* infection in the mouse lung. With its elimination, longevity has improved enormously. I must state that the specimens I am using do not reflect the current state of the ICI animal colonies.

An example of a disease that is now uncommon is ectromelia (mouse pox) (Fig. 2).

I have also chosen to illustrate rat leprosy because of its rarity. The 'leprae cells' are macrophages. Fig. 3 shows 'leprae' cells packed with mycobacterium.

Fig. 4 shows a lung from a rat infected with *Corynebacterium kutscheri,* the organism of the disease pseudotuberculosis in this species. It also affected the liver, kidney, and tibiotarsal joint of the animal. In guinea pigs, rabbits, and primates the disease of this name is caused by *Yersinia pseudotuberculosis.* A pulmonary abscess is illustrated (Fig. 5), and at higher power clumps of organisms may be seen (Fig. 6).

We must continue to be vigilant, however; latent infections may affect other susceptible strains and species, including man.

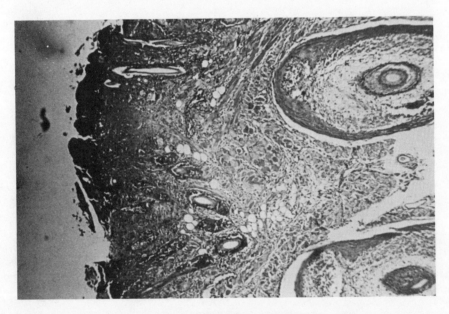

Fig. 2 – Ectromelia (mouse pox).

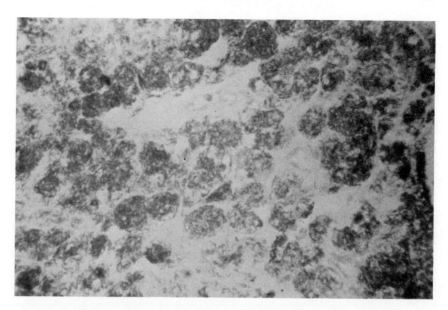

Fig. 3 – 'Leprae' cells as macrophages packed with mycobacterium.

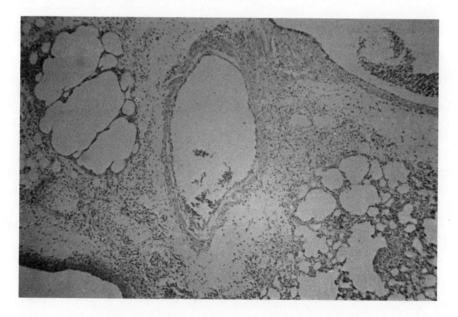

Fig. 4 – Rat lung infected with *Corynebacterium kutscheri*.

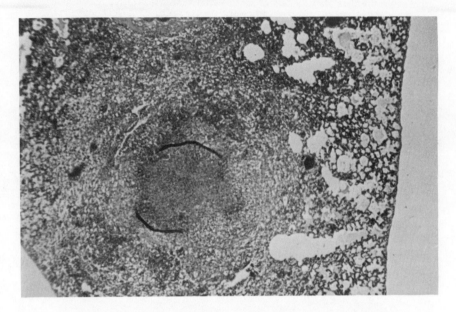

Fig. 5 – Pulmonary abscess caused by *Yersinia pseudotuberculosis*.

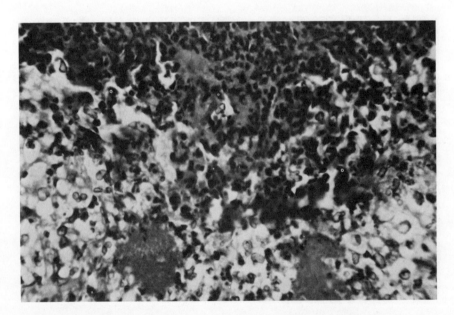

Fig. 6 – Pulmonary abscess with clumps of *Y. pseudotuberculosis* visible.

DISEASES OF LABORATORY ANIMALS THAT ARE TRANSMISSIBLE TO OTHER SPECIES

I have already mentioned primates and man. Some specific infections, including some that may be latent in animals, may be transmitted to man. I would like to illustrate this quickly with lymphocytic meningitis viral infection. The risks of this disease to man have been mentioned by Sebesteny (see the following contribution in this volume). Mononuclear cell inflammatory exudate in the meninges is illustrated (Figs 7 and 8).

Another risk to man is tuberculosis. Fortunately it is rare these days, but may still be met in imported monkeys. The illustration shows a caseated lesion with necrosis (Fig. 9), endotheleoid cells, mononuclears, and fibrosis. At higher magnification (Fig. 10) giant cells may be seen.

Salmonellosis may cause devastating epizootics. A lesion from a guinea pig liver affected by *S. typhimurium* is illustrated (Fig. 11). A colony may become infected from contaminated food.

IMPORTANCE OF DIETARY CONTROL

We have now defined the environment carefully, setting standards for temperature, humidity. lighting, cage size, etc. In addition to the physical conditions, the importance of the diet has been recognised.

To illustrate the importance of diet I have chosen three examples. The first is the well-known effect of vitamin C deficiency in species that cannot synthesise it. Examples of such species are the guinea pig and primates. Ascorbic acid is essential to the formation of osteoid, dentine, and collagen. In scorbutic rickets the usual orderly array of structures seen in normal animals is distorted by decreased osteoid decomposition in the calcified cartilage, disrupting ossification.

I must now mention the work of Tannenbaum & Silverstone (1949) and of our Chairman who, with Dr Tucker (Table 1), showed that restriction of the diet significantly alters the incidence of tumours in rodents. Groups of 40 mice were allowed either unrestricted feeding for 18 months, or received a ration of 5 g/day for the same period. Restriction resulted in a reduction in the total number of tumours, and specifically liver and lymphoreticular tumours.

Chronic progressive glomerulonephritis of the rat is a well-known condition. There is an entirely different condition called intratubular microlithiasis manifest as laminated casts at the cortico-medullary junction of the kidney, predominantly in females. The affected part

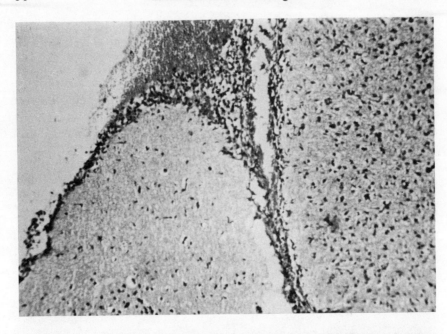

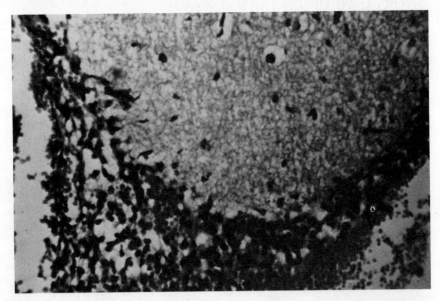

Figs 7 & 8 – Mononuclear cell inflammatory exudate in the meninges.

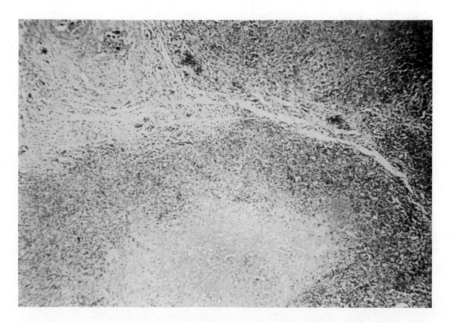

Fig. 9 – Lesion with necrosis, endotheleoid cells, mononuclears and fibrosis due to tuberculosis.

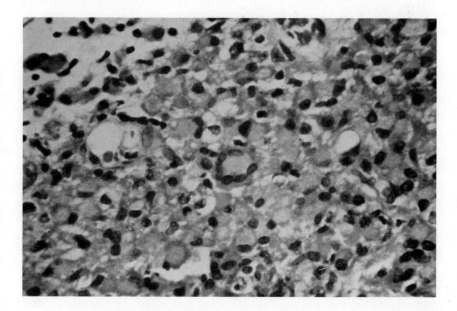

Fig. 10 – Higher magnification of Fig. 9 showing giant cells.

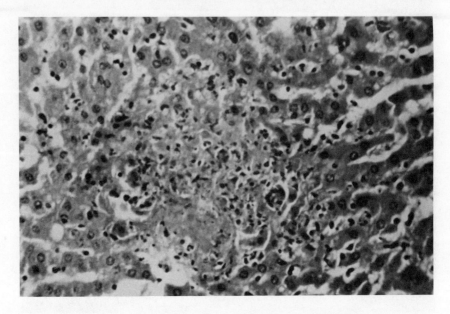

Fig.11 – Guinea pig liver infected with *Salmonella typhimurium*.

Table 1 – Reduction of tumour incidence in mice by dietary restriction.

Feeding	Total tumours by 18 months	Liver tumours	Lung tumours	Lympho-reticular neoplasms	Other neoplasms
5 g diet/day 1 mouse/cage	4	2	0	1	1
Diet *ad libitum* 1 mouse/cage	32	15	2	11	2 testis 1 kidney 1 thyroid

(From Roe & Tucker 1980)

of the kidney is usually relatively small. Oestrogens and mineral excretion are important in the incidence and severity, and if testing medicines, drugs altering tubular secretion alter the incidence and severity.

THE INFLUENCE OF GENETIC FACTORS

We are now aware (although I suspect still not sufficiently) of the interactions with the genome, and that these affect our tests. There is also debate on the relative merits of using inbred, outbred, and crosses of inbred rodent strains for testing for oncogenic potential of chemicals.

An example of genetic defect is hypotrichiasis of rats. Rats that are homozygous for this recessive gene develop a natural coat to 20 days and then lose it after 3–4 weeks developing hyperkeratosis of sebaceous glands.

Osteoarthritis is another familial condition but affecting mice. Table 2 shows the incidence of squamous cell carcinomas of the mouth. Buckley *et al.* (1980) reported that an inbred strain derived from the Alderley Park rat has an incidence of 50 per cent, whereas an outbred strain from which it was derived had only 5 per cent. These authors suggest dietary husks in the pharynx contribute to the condition.

Table 2 – Incidence of squamous cell carcinomas of the oral cavity in untreated rats.

H.M.T. strain	50% tumours	Inbred
Harwell Outbred Wistar Rats	5% tumours	Outbred

(From Buckley *et al.* 1980)

DETERMINATION OF DISEASE BY THE INCIDENCE OF CIRCUMSTANCES

Unfortunately, although very considerable progress has been made with controlling many of these entities, there are still a large number that remain extant or ill-understood. One of the difficulties in advancing our understanding results from the complex interaction of some of the elements, which initiate or modify infectious and degenerative diseases or the formation of tumours.

An example of this centres around the stomach worm *Gonglyonema neoplasticum*. The proliferative lesions are carcinoma-like and were first thought to be a tumour as a result of parasitism. Proof of this was considered to be the squamous lesions observed in the lung by Fibiger and presumed to be metastases. Current opinion suggests the condition was a non-tumour epithelial proliferative response to vitamin A deficiency, exacerbated by the presence of the parasite, thus affecting both stomach and lung.

A more serious problem is that of Tyzzer's disease, caused by *Bacillus piliformis*. It may cause fatal epizootics or lie latent waiting for some exacerbating factor such as overcrowding, poor sanitation, tumour transplantation, irradiation, oral administration of sulphanilamides or cortisone. The latter may be used to detect latent infection. It affects most laboratory species, and if we needed any other reason not to house species jointly in a Noah's Ark then this is it. A lesion in mouse liver is illustrated (Fig. 12) and a similar one from the rabbit (Fig. 13). It also affects the bowel (Fig. 14) and heart. Interactions between organisms occur. A well-known example is the murine hepatitis virus (MHV) and the protozoon *Eperythrozoon coccoides*. Some strains of MHV, e.g. strains II and III, are exacerbated by non-specific stress, but strain MHVI acts in concert with *E. coccoides* to produce liver and splenic necrosis.

Much of the variability of the model within the same laboratory and between laboratories may result from these interactions. When several laboratories share the same source of animals, then they may share some of the experience with age-related change and tumour incidence. On the other hand, the specific conditions of the laboratory may be the dominant factor, and differences in data result between laboratories or within the same laboratory using a particular strain of rodent.

Fig. 12 – Liver lesion in the mouse due to Tyzzer's disease.

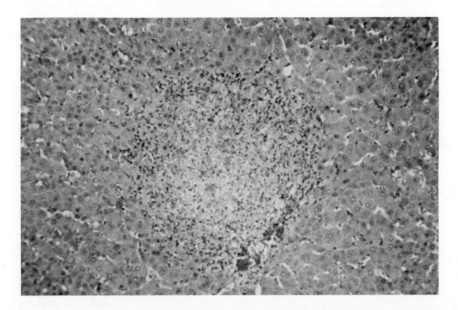

Fig. 13 – Liver lesion in the rabbit due to Tyzzer's disease.

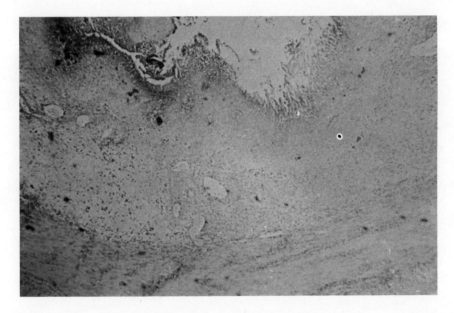

Fig. 14 – Tyzzer's disease in the bowel.

As most testing laboratories have physical separation of their animal source from the test area, either because they purchase animals or because they have a separate breeding unit, I will refer to factors incurred before acquisition by the test area as 'initial factors' and ones following transfer as 'in-use' factors.

To the pathologist involved with toxicity testing, both 'initial' and 'in-use' factors may interfere with or even vitiate the experiment. These factors may include parasites, infections, dietary imbalance, injury from physical agents, degenerative diseases, tumours, familial disease, adventitous exposure to chemicals, etc.

To further illustrate the interference by disease, reference will be made to two primate diseases. Firstly, *Hepatocystis kochi* in *Cercopithecus aethiops*. This monkey malaria has extra-erythrocytic schizogony. The hepatic nodules illustrated (Fig. 15) are merocysts.

The next illustration (Fig. 16) shows pulmonary multinucleate cells with intranuclear inclusion bodies due to a 'monkey measles' myxovirus.

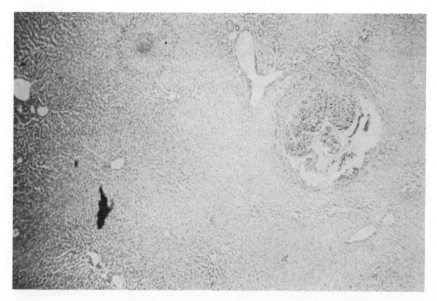

Fig. 15 – Hepatic nodules in the monkey due to *Hepatocystis kochi*.

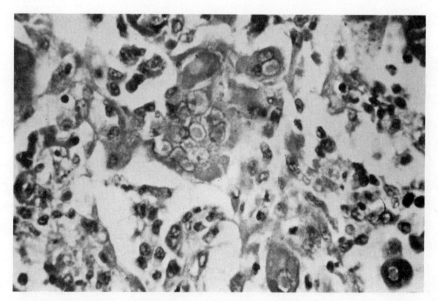

Fig. 16 – Pulmonary multinucleate cells with intranuclear inclusion bodies due to
myxovirus infection in the monkey.

Status spongiosis is a degenerative disease of unknown aetiology in the rat. In comparison the lesion illustrated in Fig. 17 was due to dosing rats with hexachlorophene. It is therefore possible to see how the former could vitiate neurotoxicity research.

I will give you an example of a problem that commences as an 'initial factor' but ends as an 'in-use' problem.

Coccidiosis may be brought into the testing facility with a new batch of rabbits. *Eimeria stiedae* infects the biliary system. Coccidiosis does, of course, also affect the intestine. *Eimeria magna* is illustrated in Fig. 18. Because of the difficulty of eradicating coccidiosis from rabbits I believe most diet manufacturers incorporate a coccidiostat in the diet – a matter for the testing facility toxicologist/pathologist to remember.

An 'in-use' environmental factor that may cause problems is light intensity. Lighting conditions considered natural for man may produce actinic retinal degeneration in albino rats, and as little as 32 lux over a period of three years may produce degeneration.

The normal retina has regular rows of cells. The degenerative retina is illustrated in Fig. 19. Some retinotoxic effects are very subtle, as illustrated by the effects of chloroquine (Gregory *et al.*) on the ganglion cells of rats. If actinic degeneration were present it would vitiate the model for testing for the chemical's effect.

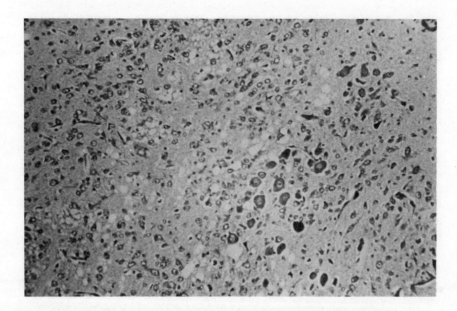

Fig. 17 – Status spongiosis due to dosing rats with hexachlorophene.

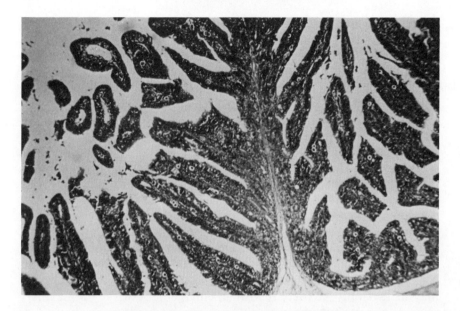

Fig. 18 – *Eimeria magna* infection of the rabbit intestine.

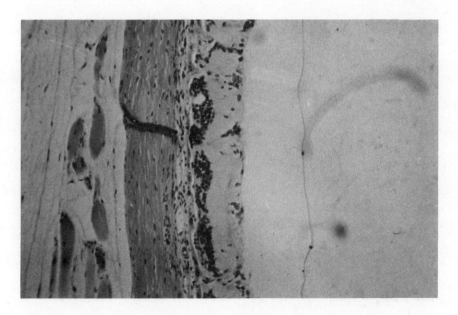

Fig. 19 – Degenerative retina in the albino rat.

It has been recognised for a long time that chloroform should not be used in the animal house environment. The liver (Fig. 20) and kidney (Fig. 21) from a mouse accidentally exposed to low levels of chloroform vapour are illustrated.

It must be recognised that although many conditions may be controlled, there are others which, with the current state of our knowledge or our freedom to act, do not yet allow us the desired control.

Sendai viral infections are all too familiar to us. I would like to show you that although the acute effects may be devastating to young animals, there are more insidious effects of interest to the pathologist. Mice that have Sendai virus infection or survive an acute attack may develop proliferative lesions in the lung. These lesions have a passing resemblance to adenomas, that is tumours, and although they should not be mistaken for such, we have not yet fully investigated their biology and interactions.

Dr Turnbull mentioned sialodacryoadenitis virus. Clinically this may in fact only be present with an enlargement of the submaxillary salivary glands, but in my work I am much less sanguine about it, as it may result in chronic corneal or conjunctival lesions that could be ascribed to a drug. Lesions in the Harderian gland (Fig. 22) and of the cornea (Fig. 23) are illustrated.

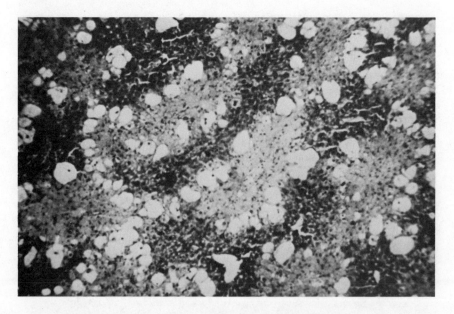

Fig. 20 – Liver from a mouse accidentally exposed to chloroform vapour.

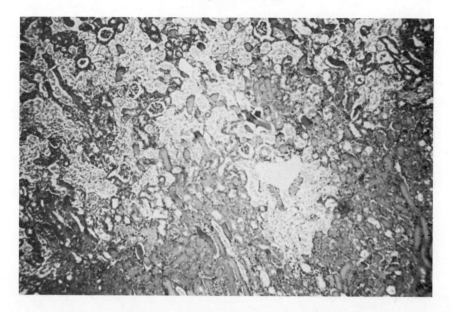

Fig. 21 – Kidney from a mouse accidentally exposed to chloroform vapour.

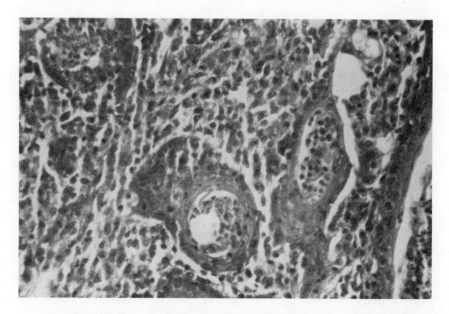

Fig. 22 – Lesion of the Harderian gland due to infection with sialodacryoadenitis virus.

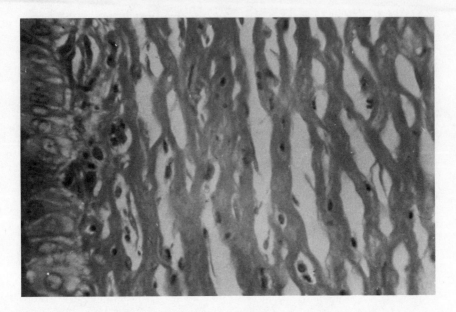

Fig. 23 – Lesion of the cornea due to infection with sialodacryoadenitis virus.

Amongst the most complex, perplexing, and important are the strain differences observed with tumour types and incidences – and the way in which these drift with time. For example, the Fischer (F344) strain of rat has a very high incidence of testicular interstitial cell tumours which approaches 90 per cent, whereas the Alderley Park Wistar rat (Alpk) has about 7 per cent. Similarly the F344 has an incidence of liver tumours of 0.7–1.2 per cent, whereas the Alpk has less than this range.

With the current state of the art, it is essential to specify the experimental conditions in the particular laboratory very carefully and then only change them with a particular objective in view.

As animals, particularly SPF animals, may be very susceptible to changes in their microorganism burden, I believe it is essential that microbiological monitoring is done regularly, so that some of the limitations of the testing model are identified.

Let us continue to remember these limitations and the variability between the available testing models, to ensure that we select the most apposite and reliable system for each research or testing programme.

REFERENCES

Buckley, P., Hulse, E. V. & Keep, R. M. (1980) *Brit. J. Cancer.*, **41**, 295–301.

Gregory, M. H., Rutty, D. A. & Wood, R. D. (1970) *J. Pathol.*, **120**, 139–150.

Roe, F. J. C. & Tucker, M. J. (1973) Recent developments in the design of carcinogenicity tests on laboratory animals. *Excerpta Medica International Congress Series* No. 311, pp. 171–177.

Tannenbaum, A. & Silverstone, H. (1949) *Cancer Res.* **9**, 724.

3

The needs of the Cancer Research Worker

A. Sebesteny, Imperial Cancer Research Fund, PO Box No. 123, Lincoln's Inn Fields, London WC2A 3PX

THE NATURE OF CANCER RESEARCH

There are three types of life form: unicellular, where the individual organism is relating only to its environment; multicellular, where the individual cells and their functions are regulated directly or indirectly (contact, humoral, or nervous influences) by other cells of the organism; and neoplasia where individual cells of a multicellular organism ignore or distort regulatory influences from other cells.

Cancer research is aimed at unravelling the mechanism of neoplasia, but studies involving models of the other two life forms can greatly contribute to its understanding. It therefore not only involves physicians, surgeons and medical pathologists, but also increasingly zoologists, microbiologists and, most recently, biochemists. This means a vast diversification of research work reflected by the fact that in our institute three divisions, five units, and one extra-mural unit functioning sixteen years ago have now grown to forty departments (now modestly called 'laboratories') apart from five extra-mural units. Projects relevant to cancer research do not only come under an increasing number of individual disciplines (such as those indicated by 1–8 on Fig. 1), but many of them involve several disciplines either by extension of the sphere of the work or by collaboration (such as those indicated by numbers 9–15 on Fig. 1).

The aim of most research projects may be initially founded on the study of either aetiology, pathology, diagnosis, therapy, or prevention; but invariably these are interrelated, and progress in one may give a pointer or stimulus towards another aim (Fig. 2). For example the finding of the consumption of certain grasses containing silica fibres

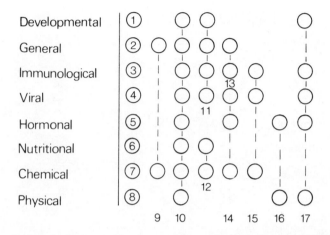

Developmental
General
Immunological
Viral
Hormonal
Nutritional
Chemical
Physical

9   10   14   15   16   17

Fig. 1 – Examples of cancer research projects fitting into various disciplines
(represented with a ring):

1. Developmental: study of multicellular reproduction, cellular interaction, tissue or tumour formation and organ development; e.g. slime moulds, tissue and organ cultures, amphibian metamorphosis and regeneration, tumour pathology.
2. Genetic: study of coding and its expression in unicellular, germ and somatic cells: e.g. bacteria, Drosophila, human HLA system.
3. Immunological: e.g. study of tumour antigens.
4. Viral: e.g. study of viruses as models of gene expression.
5. Hormonal: study of hormonal influences on malignancy; e.g. the correlation of female sex hormone levels with mammary cancer incidence.
6. Nutritional: e.g. study of the correlation of food intake with cancer incidence.
7. Chemical: e.g. study of chemical carcinogens.
8. Physical: e.g. carcinogenicity of asbestos or irradiation.
9. Genetic-chemical: e.g. the study of mutagenicity of chemical carcinogens.
10. Multidisciplinary: e.g. the study of ageing, or pathology or chemotherapy of cancer may involve all disciplines.
11. Viral tumourgenesis involves developmental, genetic, immunological and viral studies.
12. Nutritional and biochemical: e.g. the study of vitamin A serum levels in relation to cancer incidence.
13. Genetic basis of immunology: e.g. the study of immunological phenomena in congenic resistant mouse strains.
14. E.g. the study of murine mammary tumour virus in mouse tumours induced by a combination of chemical and mammotropic hormones.
15. E.g. the study of immunodepression caused by urethane-induced murine leukaemia virus.
16. E.g. the study of the radiosensitising effect of insulin on lung tumour metastases in X-ray irradiated mice.
17. E.g. the study of the effects of irradiation, viral infection, and hormonal influences on the development or immunology of human tumour xenografts in nude mice.

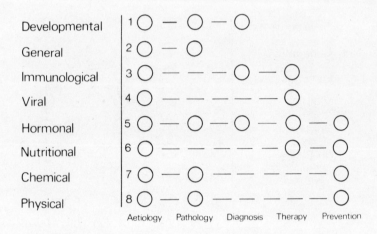

Fig. 2 – Examples of undisciplinary studies with possible aims additional to the study of aetiology of cancer.

1. Developmental studies may also involve the pathology and diagnosis of malignancy: e.g. the recognition of malignant cells in cervical smears.
2. Genetic studies may throw light on the pathology of neoplasia.
3. Immunological studies gave valuable tools for the classification and diagnosis of myeloid leukaemias and they may provide means of targeting anticancer drugs to malignant cells.
4. Viral studies revealed the possible suitability of Interferon for cancer therapy.
5. Hormonal studies revealed the role of sex hormones in the pathology of cancer, their levels were shown to be significant for diagnosis, therapy and prevention.
6. Studies show that vitamin A intake may have a role in therapy and prevention of neoplasia.
7 and 8. Physical and chemical carcinogens are used for pathological studies, and their detection and avoidance is an obvious preventative measure. The graphical representation of the aims involved in multidisciplinary studies is better left to the imagination.

as an aetiological factor in a strikingly high incidence of oesophageal cancer in Turkestan, inherently carries preventative implications.

Projects plotting in a coordinate system, one axis representing the disciplines, the other the aims, could mostly be represented only by rather elaborate patches. However, there is a third consideration, methodology, which requires a third coordinate, resulting in a three-dimensional coordinate system where projects can be represented in complex and bizarre spatial shapes (Fig. 3).

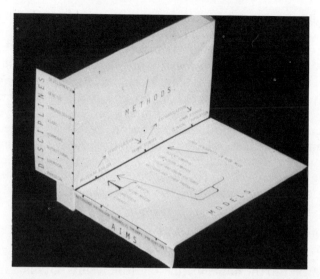

Fig. 3 – Representation of the methods of cancer research as a 3rd coordinate. It ranges from studies in man (population statistics and clinical trials) to those in molecular biology. Use of animals occupies the central position and includes the verification of findings and hypotheses of molecular biology, extrapolation from animal models to human cancer, bearing human tumour xenografts and supplying tools and *in vitro* models for molecular biology together with non-mammalian animals and unicellular organisms.

METHODS USED IN CANCER RESEARCH

The methods of cancer research range from studies of human populations or clinical cases at one end of the scale, to the molecular level of biochemical phenomena at the other end of the scale, in the search for the trigger mechanism which transforms cells from those obeying the rules of reproduction and tissue formation to malignant cells no longer doing so. It is not by deliberate design that the methods involving laboratory animals happen to occupy the central section of the methodology 'coordinate', as they interrelate with both ends of the scale: findings in the field of molecular biology often need confirmation in organised living systems with unimpaired cellular, humoral, and nervous interactions; laboratory animals also present many models of human biology and of human cancer from which extrapolations can be made, with strict reservations in view of inter-species differences; human cancer itself can also be grown in immuno-compromised laboratory animals (such as nude mice), a step in the reverse direction for bridging these differences; finally, laboratory animals provide numerous *in vitro* models (embryos, tissue and organ cultures) and biological tools (cell hybrids, cell components, sera, blood and ascitic fluid) for molecular biology studies along-side non-mammalian animals such as Drosophila (which has a low number of chromosomes with easily manipulated, well studied genes) amphibia (capable of metamorphosis and regeneration), slime moulds (a transitional system between mono and multicellular organisms), bacteria, viruses (comparatively simple, fast-producing systems of genetic coding, translation and expression, available in large numbers and amenable to manipulation), and oncogenic viruses (involved in transformation of non-malignant cells). These systems are increasingly providing models for molecular biology, a highly desirable and welcome step towards reducing the *in vivo* use of animals.

EXTRAPOLATION FROM LABORATORY MODELS TO HUMAN CANCER

Extrapolation to the human situation from results obtained in animals in *in vivo* experiments was the prevailing approach in the earlier days of cancer research. With the advent of molecular biology it became necessary also to verify hypotheses and *in vitro* findings in animal experiments. Small laboratory animals reproduce at a high rate, require comparatively small space for the accommodation of large numbers, and the disadvantages of species difference between them and man are counterbalanced by the quantitatively meaningful results obtainable from a large and uniform population under uniform husbandry and environment, particularly if inbred animals are used. In the early days conventional animals were readily accepted for this purpose without complaint, provided no mortality or clinical disease interfered with the results. In fact, there was a strong school of thought that conventional animals were more comparable with man because he is not to be regarded as SPF. Immunologists in particular subscribed to this; yet paradoxically, in our institute at any rate, Immunology was the department converted the most rapidly and decisively to the opposite view. Their department attempted to work with two categories of animals at once: abundant category 4 SPF mice from our breeding unit, and animals of lower microbiological quality from other sources. As well as obtaining different results from these two categories of animals a third category of animals provided the most spectacular anomalies in expected immunological phenomena: SPF animals freshly exposed on arrival to agents brought in by animals from other sources. In particular, infestation with intestinal flagellates caused a high degree of activation of the macro-phage system (Sebesteny 1974) associated with an increased RNA metabolism (Keast & Chesterman 1972) apart from obvious clinical or sub-clinical disease (Sebesteny 1969). Other problems included two explosive outbreaks of ectromelia and persistent endemic infection with Sendai virus. A large proportion of SPF mice in this department are now housed and used in eight experimental isolators, where they retain their freedom from pathogens.

Studies on ageing involve keeping animals to natural death. However, death of animals due to infections endemic in a conventional population can hardly be described as 'natural', especially if it is due to debilitation and self-mutilation caused by mite infestation or it involves the very organs under study: for instance bulbo-urethral glands with abscesses due to *Pasteurella pneumotropica* (Sebesteny 1973) in animals used for the study of changes in the male reproductive apparatus due to age, or livers with Tyzzer's disease in animals used for the study of RNA metabolism in liver cells. Consequently these groups of workers have been using SPF animals kept under barrier conditions throughout the studies, and were quite prepared to run down and reestablish large new groups of animals under long-term studies when the above infections entered inadvertently.

The use of transplantable tumours had been and still is an important aspect of cancer research. Contamination by infective agents has frequently plagued this type of work. Such agents ranged from ectromelia virus causing major epidemics with high losses, and polyoma virus causing gross alteration in the growth rate and composition of transplanted tumours, to bacterial infections with *Pasteurella pneumotropica, Staphylococcus aureus, Escherichia coli,* or *Proteus mirabilis.* A significant proportion of these agents are absent from SPF animals, thus reducing the risk of infection of tumours with the host's flora. However, risk of infection with *Staphylococcus aureus* and Enterobacteriaceae still remains in SPF animals, and *Proteus mirabilis* strains found in various infected tumours corresponded to those carried by their hosts by Dienes typing (Fig. 4; Story 1954) which highlighted the importance of host flora in tumour contamination.

The induction of viral tumours is often carried out in newborn mice. A moderate level of pre-weaning losses due to infantile diarrhoea in a breeding colony might be a tolerable nuisance only, but when more than 50% of neonates inoculated at birth with an oncogenic virus were lost in the experimental animal house, where infection with mouse hepatitis virus was prevalent, action was called for. This type of work is now carried out in positive pressure isolators using SPF mice, with no losses.

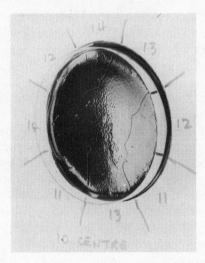

Fig. 4 – – Dienes typing of *Proteus mirabilis* strains on blood agar plate: swarms
of identical strains merge while a distinct groove is visible between swarms of
non-identical strains.

However, objections to the use of SPF animals are not entirely
unjustifiable. Most SPF hysterectomy-derivation programmes start
with a germ-free status followed by the introduction of an arbitrarily
chosen initial flora of nonpathogenic organisms thought to be
beneficial to the species concerned. On to this flora a gradual build-up
of human and environmental organisms follows in the SPF breeding
unit. This flora may turn out to be quite different from the original
conventional one. This could result in different biochemical processes
in the alimentary tract involving the utilisation of food components,
production of vitamins, and processes of detoxication and drug
conversion, which may give different experimental results from those
previously obtained in conventional animals. Furthermore, the diet
of SPF animals is usually subjected to some sterilisation process
(e.g. heat or gamma irradiation) which may alter a number of
dietary constituents playing a part in bacterial or host metabolism.
We had first-hand experience of vitamin K deficiency manifesting
as haemorrhages in mice after the establishment of SPF breeding
colonies and vitamin E deficiency manifesting as muscular dystrophy
after the establishment of the SPF rabbit breeding colony. Dietary
supplements of these vitamins eliminated the above conditions, but
many experimenters expressed concern, as the level of these vitamins
in the diet is thought to have an influence on tumour growth *in vivo*.

On the positive side the reduction in mortality due to the elimination of endemic diseases together with the focusing of attention upon dietary problems can reveal background dietary problems unconnected with sterilisation and hitherto unrecognised, such as a high incidence of hair-balls due to lack of roughage (Sebesteny 1977) and soft tissue calcification due to high vitamin D content in the diet of SPF rabbits. A survey of 31 European diets showed vitamin D contents ranging from 40 to 6000 IU per kilogram! When vitamin D supplementation in our rabbit diet was reduced from 2800 IU/kg to 0, the problem of soft-tissue calcification ceased.

The strongest argument against the use of SPF animals applies in the case of inbred strains of mice with a spontaneous mammary tumour incidence, in the aetiology of which retroviruses passed in the maternal milk to the off-spring are involved. Hysterectomy-derivation and cross-fostering prevents the transmission of these agents. Our first attempt to reestablish a mammary tumour incidence of 90% by 8 months of age in the hysterectomy-derived counterparts of conventional C3H/Avy mice has met with only partial success. Intraperitoneal injection of purified virus into newborn SPF C3H/Avy mice resulted in a colony where the tumour incidence reached 48% at 8 months of age, while in non-injected SPF mice a tumour incidence of 8–28% prevailed at 16 months of age (Tan & Sebesteny 1972). At present we are attempting to reestablish a viral pregnancy-dependent mammary tumour incidence in SPF BR6 mice.

THE VALUE OF GROWING HUMAN TUMOURS AS TRANSPLANTS IN IMMUNO-COMPROMISED ANIMALS

The establishment, growth, and transplantation of human tumours in immuno-compromised animals, in particular in athymic nude mice (Sebesteny *et al.* 1979) was a major step in reducing the gap due to species differences between man and animals. These animals are highly susceptible to infections, particularly to viruses such as Sendai virus (Ward *et al.* 1976), mouse hepatitis virus (Sebesteny & Hill 1974; McKenzie *et al.* 1978) and polyoma virus (Sebesteny *et al.* 1980). The latter also modified tumour growth by promoting the proliferation of murine stroma at the expense of human cancer cells in the xenografts, and produced skin tumours unconnected with the human tumour xenografts, apart from causing the wasting and demyelinating disease described. SPF status including freedom from these viruses is essential for these hosts of human tumour xenografts, and we exclusively house and use them in twelve experimental isolators, under constant monitoring.

ANIMALS AS A SOURCE OF TISSUES
AND BIOLOGICAL PRODUCTS

Tissues and biological products from laboratory animals are increasingly used, together with viruses, bacteria, slime moulds, and non-mammallian species, for the supply of models for molecular biology studies. This is the most acceptable use of these animals to those opposing animal experimentation as it obviates *in vivo* experiments, and involves only humane killing. At first sight it should not appear critical whether tissue or fluids taken aseptically, and as a rule from sites without a bacterial flora, come from conventional or SPF animals. However, invasion by bacteria or carriage of latent viruses could occur in normally sterile tissues of the body without evidence of clinical illness, and the inclusion of tissues or body fluids from just one such animal could infect the whole batch of primary tissue or organ culture or other *in vitro* system. An agent had been implicated as a suspected cause of human leukaemia until it was identified as *Mycoplasma pulmonis* presumably arising from murine tissue used tissue cultures, are deemed to be sterile, yet several pathogens are now known to be able to cross the placental barrier especially in stressed or sub-clinically affected animals, such as lymphocytic chorio-meningitis virus (a possible agent of zoonosis), *Mycoplasma* or *Bacillus piliformis* (Fries 1978, 1979), or at least to be present in the wall or the lumen of the uterus; of 56 apparently normal 12–15 day pregnant mouse uteri examined 2 yielded *Pasteurella pneumotropica,* 2 lactobacillus sp., and 1 a streptococcus sp. (Sebesteny & Lee 1973). Tissue culture workers are increasingly aware of the nuisance of contamination by microbial agents and in particular by lymphocytic choriomeningitis virus, presenting a serious risk to themselves. We monitor all mouse stocks for its absence.

Another non-experimental use of animals is serum production. For *in vitro* work antibodies are required to an ever-increasing spectrum of cell components or products, toxic or carcinogenic substances, antigens, immunoglobulins, hormones, viruses, proteins, enzymes, nucleic acid fractions, etc. These are extracted and purified with a great deal of effort and often in minute quantities, and their loss through intercurrent disease killing or diminishing the response of the challenged animal would be far more serious than the extra cost of using disease-free rabbits for serum production or, more recently, SPF mice for monoclonal antibody production. The old 'conventional school' believed that diseased rabbits were better antibody producers than healthy ones. We have no numerical evidence yet to the contrary other than our experience that since the exclusive use of SPF rabbits the number of rabbits used per single antigen has gradually diminished. This may represent an increased confidence of users not only in their better survival of the immunising schedule but also in an improved response to the challenge.

RECOGNITION OF THE ADVANTAGES OF USING CLEAN ANIMALS

The requirements of SPF animals for cancer research may not be as clear-cut and obvious as for toxicological testing. It took a continuous supply of SPF animals for a long period to demonstrate their advantages to research workers who came and left during the years. Their advantage was not necessarily clear to those who came, but I had numerous pleas for supplies of our animals to those who had left for other institutes which used conventional animals.

Many cancer research workers have not only learned to prefer and demand microbiologically clean animals; they also have required uniformity in genetic make-up and nutritional status. Furthermore they have expected stability in these parameters, as well as prompt supply of the desired animals. Repeated comparative costing exercises showed hardly any difference between the policies of purchasing or breeding our own animals. However, the above extra requirements, which we were nearly always able to satisfy, did tip the balance considerably in favour of breeding our own supply. Nevertheless on occasions we had to turn to outside sources; we could not keep in step with the ever-increasing demand for newer and newer congenic strains of mice. Furthermore in the present economic climate we felt compelled to breed only to existing known demand. With the increasing numbers of short-term visiting scientists and PhD students who could not afford to wait for the adjustment of the breeding programme to their requirements, occasional batches of animals had to be bought in to start off their work. Before we started breeding our own nude mice we bought them, but lost them owing to Sendai virus infection, which was eventually traced back to source.

QUALITY CONTROL IN THE SUPPLY OF LABORATORY ANIMALS: THE NEED FOR A NEW ORGANISATION TO TAKE OVER THE WORK OF THE LABORATORY ANIMALS CENTRE

To those engaged in fundamental research and probably to others too, the use of a centralised quality control and monitoring service gives the greatest confidence. This had been provided so far by the

Laboratory Animals Centre, which I did not hesitate to call upon in need. The discontinuation of this service is a sad loss despite its limited capacity to deal with all aspects of monitoring to a quantitatively significant level. However, having shown the way, it opened up new possibilities for an even more efficient substitute; alternatively it may surrender quality control and monitoring to commercial enterprise. In the name of the fundamental research worker I rather hope that the latter will not be the case. Quality control and monitoring is an open science, ready for improvement, innovations, and cross-fertilisation of ideas, preferably day to day. Its aim is to prove credibly the absence of pathogenic microorganisms (which is much more difficult than to demonstrate their presence!) from a large group of animals, using samples with severe practical limitations in quantity, frequency, and in the promptness of processing. These limitations can be compensated for by increased reliability in methods of preservation, isolation, and demonstration. This requires constant research, liberal use of controls, free exchange of ideas, prompt publication of innovations, and the ready availability of all details of methods used: otherwise a report stating that 'no organism X has been isolated' is relatively meaningless. Colonies grown only anaerobically with 5% CO_2 from specimens from sick guinea pigs showing typical streptococci on Gram smear could have been dismissed as those of an anaerobic streptococcus, had the original specimens not been stained to show typical diplococci, had the organism not been shown to grow even better in air with 10% CO_2 giving biochemical reactions typical of pneumococcus (Sebesteny 1978), and had a literature search not been undertaken to reveal a solitary report of a carboxyphilic pneumococcus (Austrian & Collins 1966). An anaerobic variant of *Streptobacillus moniliformis* might not have been found in cervical abscesses of guinea pigs (Aldred *et al.* 1974) had routinely anaerobic cultures not been made. We would not have found *Listeria monocytogenes* in the brains of rabbits affected with torticollis† had we not attempted re-isolation from brain material refrigerated for several weeks. The Mycoplasma Laboratory of LAC repeatedly finds batches of media incapable of supporting the growth of murine mycoplasmata, by the regular use of positive controls.

Pressures of commercial interests, limitations in capital, and secrecy, work against the above outlined requirements for reliable quality control. I wonder if it is naive to suggest that such control might be exempted from competition, and instead shared, by using

† The person who autopsied these rabbits was subsequently ill with meningitis and lymphadenopathy for six weeks, but listeriosis was not confirmed.

either a cooperatively established central facility, or by freely exchanging ideas and results, perhaps under the aegis of LABA, IAT, LASA and its study groups, and the Gnotobiotics Club. This would benefit all participants and users.

The same could well apply to several other related fields. It serves the interests of all producers that the reputation of their animals is not compromised by infections acquired during and after delivery: freely shared improvements in isolator technology which renders work in them less cumbersome will encourage more and more users to keep experimental animals within such highly protective environments. There must exist an ideally suited diet for each species amongst the many diets with widely differing ingredients: an explosive outbreak followed by sporadic cases of bone deformities (Figs 18 a, b) observed in ten strains of our mice as well as in groups received from other sources fed on different diets can hardly be a genetic mutation but could well be due to some evasive nutritional factor. Liver cirrhosis affecting several hamster colonies (Chesterman & Pomerance 1965) after the elimination of aflatoxin, tapeworms, and wet-tail disease as possible factors still leaves room for a possible nutritional explanation. A central facility for genetic monitoring, requiring constant updating in methods, and one for embryo freezing, requiring high investment, a constant flow of work to justify it, and regular monitoring of frozen stocks for viability, could not be feasible as an individual enterprise for mere self-sufficiency.

There would be ample room left for competition in the availability of a wide selection of species and strains, in the quality of animals, in the reliability of staff and barriers ensuring it, in prompt delivery, and in the efficiency of services, documentation, and transport.

This cooperative, yet competitive, climate with the right balance prevailing in the commercial production of high-quality laboratory animals, of their diets, and of their environmental accessories could well ensure the full reliance of the fundamental research worker on commercial supplies in the future.

REFERENCES

Aldred, P., Hill, A. C. & Young, C. (1974). *Lab. An.* 8, 275–277.
Austrian, R. & Collins, P. (1966). *J. Bact.* 92, 1281–1284.
Chesterman, F. C. & Pomerance, A. (1965). *Brit. J. Cancer,* 19, 802–811.
Keast, D. & Chesterman, F. C. (1972). *Lab. An.* 6, 33–39.
McKenzie, R. A., Parker, R. J. & Eaves, F. W. (1978). *Lab. An.* 12, 27–28.

Schaich Fries, A. (1978). *Lab. An.* **12**, 23–26.
Schaich Fries, A. (1979). *Lab. An.* **13**, 43–46.
Sebesteny, A. (1969). *Lab. An.* **3**, 71–77.
Sebesteny, A. (1973). *Lab. An.* **7**, 315–317.
Sebestany, A. (1974). *Lab. An.* **8**, 79–81.
Sebesteny, A. (1977). *Lab. An.* **11**, 135.
Sebesteny, A. (1978). *Lab. An.* **12**, 181–183.
Sebesteny, A. & Hill, A. (1974). *Lab. An.* **8**, 317–326.
Sebesteny, A. & Lee, P. (1973). *Lab. An.* **7**, 271–277.
Sebesteny, A., Taylor-Papadinitrious, J., Ceriani, R., Millis, R., Schmitt, C. & Trevan, D. (1979). *J. Natl. Cancer Inst.* **63**, 1331–1337.
Sebesteny, A., Tilly, R., Balliwill, F. & Trevan, D. (1980). *Lab. An.* **14**, 337–345.
Story, P. (1954). *J. Path. Bact.* **68**, 55.
Tan, W. C. & Sebesteny, A. (1972). *Lab. An.* **6**, 1–7.
Ward, J. M., Honchens, D. P., Collins, M. J., Young, D. M. & Reagan, R. L. (1976). *Vet. Pathol.* **13**, 36–46.

4

The needs of the Parasitologist

M. J. Worms, PhD, National Institute for Medical Research, Mill Hill, London NW7 1AA

INTRODUCTION

In common with workers in other disciplines, the parasitologist requires animals of 'good' quality; a typical definition of which is "free from organisms which under any circumstances of breeding or experimentation may become pathogenic" (Box 1976). This concept of a defined status which accepts some infaunation by microorganisms places much emphasis on pathogenicity in selecting specific organisms from which an animal must be free. Classification systems used hitherto provide information on pathogenic organisms which are absent. Information on other organisms considered non-pathogenic is not readily available. Yet these organisms may have effects upon the parasites introduced experimentally.

INTERACTIONS BETWEEN PARASITES AND OTHER MICROORGANISMS

It has been known for many years that microorganisms may exert apparently nonspecific yet pronounced effects upon parasites (Cox 1978a). Such studies have largely been on the interaction of blood- and tissue-dwelling organisms. The influence of intestinal bacteria on intestinal helminths and protozoa has been less well investigated. Early studies in gnotobiotic hosts (Newton *et al.* 1959) suggest that in the absence of a gut flora, intestinal parasites may establish in host species which are poor or refractory hosts when reared conventionally. The presence of a gut flora in normally susceptible host species may, however, be favourable to parasite establishment; *Nippostrongylus brasiliensis, Aspicularis tetraptera*, and *Histomonas meleagridis* are reported to thrive better in conventional than in germ-free hosts

(Wescott & Todd 1964, Przyjalkowski 1974, Doll & Franker 1963). In mice the removal of the established flora by antibiotics and replacement by bacteria predominantly of a single genus (*Escherichia, Serratia, Proteus, Pseudomonas*) favoured the establishment of *Trichinella spiralis*, whereas replacement by others (*Lactobacillus, Bacillus mesentericus*) did not (Stefanski and Przyjalkowski, 1966). It may be that the composition of the gut flora, rather than simply the presence of such, influences parasite development and that selection of microorganisms with which to populate caesarian-derived stock is of significance in the standardisation of animals for parasitological research.

HOST-PARASITE INTERACTION

Each species of laboratory animal may serve as host to a number of different species of parasite. The complexity of the life cycles of many of these parasites limits their occurrence under laboratory conditions, and the host-parasite listings familiar in laboratory animal textbooks are thus relatively short. These lists, however, have been compiled on the basis of those parasites which complete all or a substantial part of their development in conventionally reared intact hosts. Each parasite is in this way associated with a certain range of host species. Within a restricted environment, however, all animals of all species are exposed potentially to all organisms, including parasites, present therein. The consequences of that exposure are influenced greatly by the genetic constitution of the host (Taylor & Muller 1976) and its immune competence. Increasing use is being made of animals of inbred strains, often of immunodeficient status, supplied from barrier-maintained breeding stocks. It is now well established that in some strains, parasites hitherto considered to be non-pathogenic may become pathogenic, and it appears that continuous reappraisal of host-parasite listings is desirable.

In those host-parasite combinations in which full development occurs, diagnosis of infection is usually easily made. In other host-parasite combinations, infection may be of a form in which organisms are not recoverable for diagnostic purposes, or infection may persist for a period which is not long enough for diagnosis by standard techniques. This period of infection, though perhaps brief, may nonetheless alter the status of the host. Recognition of this has led recently to the development of more sensitive diagnostic tests such as those for *Mycoplasma* and *Encephalitozoon* (Cassell *et al.* 1981; Gannon 1980), and to the suggestion that specialist veterinary diagnostic laboratories be set up to perform them (Held 1981).

Anatomical and major physiological changes in the host attributable to parasitic infection are described in standard textbooks. There is, however, an increasing awareness of subtle physiological and behavioural changes which may occur. Recent examples illustrate their great variety – effects upon exploratory and social behaviour (McNair & Timmons 1977, Freeland 1981), reduced learning ability (Witting 1979), impaired reproduction (Wayne-Moss & Camin 1970, Shaw & Quagdano 1975), lowered metabolic activity (Rosenmann & Morrison 1975), anorexia (Symons 1969), prolongation of anaesthesia (Coelho *et al.* 1977), elevation of interferon levels (Sonnenfeld & Kierszenbaum 1981), and perturbation of the immune response. In common with other microorganisms, parasites provoke specific responses by the host to their presence which may be protective and destroy or limit parasite development (Cohen & Sadun 1976). Many parasites have evolved complex mechanisms by which to circumvent these responses and thus persist in a hostile environment (Ogilvie & Wilson 1976). Parasites appear able to provoke a number of non-specific responses also. The ability to do so does not require complex parasite development (nor is it necessarily associated with high pathogenicity), yet the responses may be of significance. It has become increasingly evident that the survival, behaviour, and patho-genicity of a parasite and of the host response to infection may be influenced markedly by both specific and nonspecific responses induced by prior or concurrent infection with other organisms. Inter-actions of parasites are therefore of importance to parasitologists and are thus relevant to their needs in the standardisation of laboratory animals.

INTERACTION BETWEEN PARASITES

Interactions between organisms which share the same location may be competitive, and surveys of wild populations of hosts (Halvorsen 1976, Holmes 1973) furnish examples of apparent exclusion of or reduction in number of one species of parasite in the presence of another in the same location in the host. Further support is provided by laboratory systems. Larsh & Campbell (1952), for example, found the number of *Hymenolepis nana* which established in mice was reduced in hosts with concurrent *T. spiralis* infection. In concurrent single worm infections of *H. diminuta* and *H. citelli*, each species suffered a reduction in size (Read & Pfifer 1959). Similarly, both parasites were reduced in size and displaced from their preferred site in the intestine in concurrent infections of *H. diminuta* and

Moniliformis dubius (Holmes 1961). The mechanisms of such interactions are poorly understood. Under special circumstances a direct
competition, e.g. for nutrient resource, may be involved. Currently,
however, it appears that the effects of one parasite upon another
are achieved indirectly by way of the host's response, and that these
effects may not be uniformly adverse.

Protozoa

Much of our knowledge of parasite interaction derives from syringe
passaged experimental infections in rodents of blood parasites of the
genera *Plasmodium, Babesia,* and *Trypanosoma* (reviewed by Cox
(1978b)). Infection in this manner results in a probably nonspecific
increase in phagocytic activity of the reticuloendothelial system, and
a specific antibody-mediated anti-parasite response, which together
lead to the destruction of the parasites and development of protective
immunity. Infection is accompanied frequently by a parasite-induced
immuno-depression (Wedderburn 1974, Terry 1977, Capron & Camus
1979). Interaction between these genera is highly variable. In mice
exposed to *Plasmodium berghei* and *Trypanosoma lewisi,* the parasitaemia of both species was elevated. If infection with *T. lewisi* was made
seven days after *P. berghei* infection however, an increase only of
trypanosome parasitaemia occurred. Similar enhancing effects were
observed when near-simultaneous infections were made of *P. berghei*
and *T. musculi, P. berghei* and *Toxoplasma gondii,* and *P. yoelii* and
Leishmania enrietti in the hamster. If infection with a second parasite
is delayed until after protective imunity to a first has developed, there
is a considerable measure of cross-protection with adverse effect
on the second species, thus mice recovered from infection with
P. berghei are protected against infection with *Babesia rodhaini* or
B. microti.

These interactions extend beyond the blood compartment, and
interaction between tissue and intestinal protozoa occurs. The
invasion by *Giardia muris* which occurs spontaneously in 20% of
mice rises to 80% when infection is concurrent with *P. berghei*
(Radulescu *et al.* 1971).

It appears, therefore, that when exposure to two species of
protozoa occurs simultaneously or within a relatively short time
span, there is either a null or an enhancing effect upon either or both
parasites; if, however, infection with one species follows at some
considerable period after exposure to another, an adverse effect
occurs. A similar conclusion may be reached in the interaction
between protozoa and helminths. Phillips *et al.* (1974) observed that
in mice infected with *Trichuris muris,* host rejection of the nematode

was delayed if the mice were exposed simultaneously or within twelve days, to infection with *P. berghei, T. brucei,* or *Babesia* spp. This effect was not observed in the rat, however, and this and similar results with other systems, e.g. Mullink *et al.* (1980) suggest that the variability in effect may not depend solely on the relative timing of acquisition of parasites, but upon the species of host also.

Helminths

The parasitic helminths have relatively complex life cycles and often pass through a number of different stages during which they may present different identities to the host (Philipp *et al.* 1980). The majority provoke a host response which may or may not be effective on the destruction of tissue parasites, or expulsion of intestinal parasites. Protective immunity may be generated, and there is increasing evidence of perturbation, including depression of the host immune system (Terry 1977, Capron & Camus 1979). In immune hosts there is considerable evidence of cross-protection, i.e. an adverse interaction between unrelated organisms. A number of examples are quoted by Doy *et al.* (1981). Dineen *et al.* (1977) found that irradiated *Trichostrongylus colubriformis* protected sheep against homologous reinfection, partially protected them against the closely-related *T. vitrinus,* but not at all against *Nematododirus spathiger* when exposed to each species separately. When exposed to all three simultaneously, all were eliminated, indicating that although a specific triggering event was necessary, the host response was effective nonspecifically against all the parasites present. Bindseil & Andreassen (1981) found that in mice exposed to eggs of *Ascaris suum* seven days prior to infection with *H. diminuta,* an adverse effect on the establishment of the latter occurred. Little or no effect was observed if exposure to *A. suum* occurred earlier than seven days prior to or simultaneously with infection with *H. diminuta.* These workers suggest that it is the return of the ascarid larvae to the intestine after hepatopulmonary migration which triggers an expulsion mechanism. This coincides with the infection with *H. diminuta,* and both parasites are affected thereby. This observation emphasises the importance of the relative timing of exposure to helminth parasites also. It is of further significance in that the effect was apparently produced by a parasite undergoing only partial development in an abnormal host.

Arthropods

Despite the medical and economic importance of ectoparasites and their widespread occurrence on laboratory animals, there has been little study until recently of immunity to arthropods. The host responses appear to be of two types which may be related to the type of host–ectoparasite association. The response to ectoparasites such as fleas, gamasid mites, and mosquitoes which are in contact with the host for brief periods only whilst obtaining a blood meal, evolves with repeated exposure. Initially there is a delayed type hypersensitivity which passes with subsequent exposure through an immediate hypersensitivity to a hyposensitive state. These differing phases in the host immune response will result in different tissue reactions to the feeding of the arthropod, and it is probable that this variation may have an influence upon arthropod-transmitted parasites.

Among arthropods which enter into a more prolonged association with the host there appears to be a great variety of response. Protective immunity may develop but may be expressed either locally or generally. Cross-protection which appears to be confined to closely-related species has been reported against tick or louse infestations (see Nelson *et al.* 1977) for review.

Possible interactions between arthropods and other organisms have been little studied. Bell *et al.* (1979) found that rabbits hypersensitive to feeding of the tick *Dermacentor variabilis* showed significant resistance to *Francisella tularensis*. Conversely, Callow & Stewart (1978) found that infection with *Babesia bovis* may reduce the level of resistance achieved by infected cattle to the vector tick *Boophilus microplus*. This was attributable to immunosuppressive effects of the protozoan infection and occurred early in infection.

CONCLUSIONS

This brief survey reveals that the results of parasite interactions are complex. Although most information has been obtained from experimental systems, many of them relating to parasites of medical or veterinary importance in abnormal laboratory hosts, it is unlikely that the parasites of laboratory animals will be exempt from these interactions. The possible presence of parasites has been accepted at some levels in categorised laboratory animals (LAC 1974) and are present still in many breeding stocks (Sparrow 1976).

Much current parasitological research is directed towards improved diagnosis of parasite infection, and development of vaccines for infections of medical or veterinary importance; both areas which involve the study of the immune responses of an experimental animal. It is evident that parasitic infection affects markedly the immune status of an animal and induces a number of specific and nonspecific responses. The presence of a contaminating parasite may modify these responses and introduce variability into an experimental system.

Present evidence indicates that the most relevant responses are non-specific, and particularly the immunodepressive effects of relatively brief duration, suggesting that near coincidence of exposure to contaminant and experimentally induced parasites is necessary for significant variation to occur.

Recent changes in animal production and use may combine to bring about just such a coincidence, however. In the past, animals bred and housed under conventional conditions tended to experience infection with a wide range of organisms early in life. In modern animal practice this experience is largely deferred until the animal is transferred from the breeding to the experimental area – often involving not only a journey between two different establishments, but a transfer of barrier-maintained to minimal disease or conventional housing. First exposure to a different group of microorganisms and parasites present in the new environment may thus occur at about the time of exposure to the parasite under investigation, a possible explanation perhaps of the differing results observed in infections with the same parasite in two groups of the same strain of host, differing only in their commercial source.

Parasitologists are aware of these possibilities, and in recent reports contaminant parasites have been monitored as part of the experimental observations (Good & Miller 1976), or suggested as possible causes of difference in results between experiments (Doy *et al.* 1981). Parasites are, however, being used increasingly as model systems by workers in other disciplines. As even relatively large parasites, such as pinworms, may exist undetected for long periods in a colony unless diligently searched for (Mohn & Philipp 1981), there is now perhaps a need to extend the established regular monitoring of stock beyond the breeding unit to the experimental areas. This, coupled with a revision of the organisms searched for, will provide background information against which to assess experimental variability.

REFERENCES

Bell, J. F., Stewart, S. J. & Wikel, S. K. (1979). *Am. J. Trop. Med. Hyg.* **28** (5), 876–880.

Bindseil, E. & Andreassen, J. (1981). *Parasitology* **83**, 489–496.

Box, P. G. (1976). *Lab. Anim. Sci.* **26** (2), 334–338.

Callow, L. L. & Stewart, N. P. (1978). *Nature* **272**, 818–819.

Capron, A. & Camus, D. (1979). *Springer Sem. Immunopathol.* **2**, 69–77.

Cassell, G. H., Lindsey, J. R., Davis, J. K., Davidson, M. K., Brown, M. B. & Mayo, J. G. (1981). *Lab. Anim. Sci.* 31 (6), 676–682.

Coelho, P. M. Z., Freire, A. C. T., Araujo, F. G., Pellegrino, J. & Pereira, L. H. (1977). *Am. J. Trop. Med. Hyg.* 26 (1), 186–187.

Cohen, S. & Sadun, E. H. (1976) (Eds.). *Immunology of parasitic infections,* Blackwell Scientific Publications, London.

Cox, F. E. G. (1978a). *Nature* 273, 623–626.

Cox, F. E. G. (1978b). Concomitant infections. In: Killick–Kendrick, R. & Peters, W. (Eds.) *Rodent malaria* pp. 309–343. Academic Press, London.

Dineen, J. K., Gregg, P., Windon, R. G., Donald, A. D., & Kelly, J. D. (1977). *Int. J. Parasit.* 7, 211–215.

Doll, J. P. & Franker, C. K. (1963). *J. Parasit.* 49, 411–414.

Doy, T. G., Hughes, D. L. & Harness, E. (1981). *Parasite Immunol.* 3, 171–180.

Freeland, W. J. (1981). *Science* 213, 461–462.

Gannon, J. (1980). *Lab. Anim.* 14, 91–94.

Good, A. H., Miller, K. L. (1976). *Infect. Immun.* 14 (2), 449–456.

Halvorsen, O. (1976). Negative interaction among parasites. In: Kennedy, C. R. (Ed.) *Ecological aspects of parasitology.* pp. 99–114. North Holland Publishing, Oxford.

Held, J. R. (1981). *Bull. Wld. Hlth. Org.* 59 (4), 513–518.

Holmes, J. C. (1961). *J. Parasit.* 47, 209–216.

Holmes, J. C. (1973). *Can. J. Zool.* 51 (3), 333–347.

L. A. C. (1974). *The accreditation and recognition schemes for suppliers of laboratory animals.* Manual Series No. 1. 2nd ed. Carshalton Medical Research Council Laboratory Animals Centre.

Larsh, J. E. & Campbell, C. H. (1952). *J. Parasit.* 38 sect. 2, 20–21 (abstract).

McNair, D. M. & Timmons, E. H. (1977). *Lab. Anim. Sci.* 27, 38–42.

Mohn, G. & Philipp, E. M. (1981). *Lab. Anim.* 15, 89–95.

Mullink, J. W. M. A., Ruitenberg, E. J. & Kruizinga, W. (1980). *Lab. Anim.* 14, 127–128.

Nelson, W. A., Bell, J. F., Clifford, C. M. & Keirans, J. E. (1977). *J. Med. Entymol.* 13, 389–428.

Newton, W. L., Weinstein, P. P. & Jones, M. F. (1959). *Ann. N. Y. Acad. Sci.* 78 (1), 290–306.

Ogilvie, B. M. & Wilson, R. J. M. (1976). *Brit. med. Bull.* 32 (2), 177–181.

Philipp, M., Parkhouse, R. M. E. & Ogilvie, B. M. (1980). *Nature* 287, 538–540.

Phillips, R. S., Seley, G. & Wakelin, D. (1974). *Int. J. Parasit.* 4, 409–415.

Przyjalkowski, Z. (1974). *Acta Parasit. Polon.* **22**, 345–349.
Radulescu, S., Lupascu, Gh., Ciplea, A. G. & Cernai, M. J. (1971). *Arch. Roum. Path. Exper. Microbiol.* **30**, 405–412.
Read, C. P. & Pfifer, K. (1959). *Exp. Parasit.* **8**, 46–50.
Rosenmann, M. & Morrison, P. R. (1975). *Lab. Anim. Sci.* **25**, 62–64.
Shaw, G. L. & Quagdano, D. (1975). *Exp. Parasit.* **37**, 211–217.
Sonnenfeld, G. & Kierszenbaum, F. (1981). *Am. J. Trop. Med. Hyg.* **30**, 1189–1191.
Sparrow, S. (1976). *Lab. Anim.* **10**, 365–373.
Stefanski, W. & Przyjalkowski, Z. (1966). *Exp. Parasit.* **18**, 92–98.
Symons, E. A. (1969). *Int. Rev. Trop. Med.* **3**, 49–100.
Taylor, A. E. R. & Muller, R. (1976). *Symp. Brit. Soc. Parasit.* No. 14.
Terry, R. J. (1977). *INSERM* **72**, 161–178.
Wayne-Moss, W. & Camin, J. H. (1970). *Science* **168**, 1000–1003.
Wedderburn, N. (1974). Immunodepression produced by malarial infection in mice. In: *Parasites in the immunized host: mechanisms of survival.* Ciba Foundation Symposium 25, new series. pp. 123–135. Elsevier/North Holland.
Wescott, R. B. & Todd, A. C. (1964). *J. Parasit.* **50**, 139–143.
Witting, P. A. (1979). *Z. Parasitenk.* **61**, 29–51.

5

The needs of the Immunologist

I. M. Hunneyball, BSc, PhD, Research Department, The Boots Company PLC, Pennyfoot Street, Nottingham, NG2 3AA

SUMMARY

Various factors may influence the immune responsiveness of laboratory animals. These include infectious agents (bacteria, viruses, parasites), stress, dietary factors, and non-specific inflammation. The mechanisms by which these factors alter immune function are reviewed with reference to specific examples.

The way in which immune deviation can affect the results of immunological experiments is dependent on the type of experiment. With *in vitro* studies and short term *in vivo* experiments the main problem is variability in experimental results. With long-term *in vivo* experiments, the occurrence of infection can result in loss of animals and premature termination of experiments as well as variability in results. Specific examples of problems arising from the use of animals with latent infection are quoted.

Ideally, SPF animals with a well-defined stabilised microbial flora should be used for immunological studies. This may require specific bacterial repopulation of germ-free animals. In order to maintain the stability of the microbial flora of such animals, improvements must be sought in the transportation from breeder to user. Moreover the user and breeder should keep the animals under identical conditions (preferably barrier-maintained). Finally, a microbiological monitoring system should be devised to monitor the stability of the microbial flora.

INTRODUCTION

Within the present limits of understanding of the immune system it is impossible to define precisely the microbial standards required of laboratory animals for immunological studies. Moreover, the requirements will very much depend on the nature of the experiment, and it would be impossible to cover all types of experiment in one document. Nevertheless, the basic requirement must be animals in which the immune responsiveness will not be altered by extraneous factors either during the course of an experiment or from one experiment to another. The immune responsiveness of an animal may be influenced by various factors. Therefore, I have attempted to review these factors and the impact that they may have on experimental results, giving specific examples from my own particular field of research, namely the development of drugs capable of specifically modifying immunological responses. Finally, I have considered ways of eliminating these extraneous factors, or where this is not possible, then at least stabilising them in order to minimise experimental variation.

Many factors are known to affect the immune response, and several of these can be controlled. In fact many of the microorganisms which are known to modify immune responses have been eliminated from breeding colonies through the MRC Accreditation Scheme. However, the immunomodulatory potential of many microorganisms has yet to be determined; therefore it is impossible to define a microbial flora which would not produce immune deviation. The logical conclusion from this is to consider germ-free animals. However, studies from many laboratories have shown that such animals produce abnormal immune responses. Hence an empirical approach must be taken and a reasonable compromise reached for each particular experimental situation. This will require breeding of animals to specific requirements for specific experiments, which is bound to increase the cost of the experiments, a factor which has probably inhibited the use of such animals up till now. However, the limitations of conventional animals in immunological experiments are becoming increasingly apparent, and many laboratories have moved entirely to specified pathogen free animals.

Unfortunately, the more one controls the genetic constitution and microbial environment of laboratory animals, the further away one moves from the uncontrolled outbred human situation, and it becomes increasingly difficult to extrapolate results from the experimental situation to man. Hence one must strike a balance between the optimal conditions for the generation of interpretable laboratory data and the relevance of such conditions to the human counterpart.

FACTORS AFFECTING IMMUNE RESPONSIVENESS

Regulation of the immune system

In order to understand the ways in which immune responsiveness can be modified by extraneous factors we must first consider the mechanisms involved in the regulation of immune responses. These are shown in a simplified form in Fig. 1.

The immunoregulatory network has been well characterised in mice (Cantor & Boyse, 1977, Dutton 1980, Eardley 1980, Swain 1980). Several sub-populations of T-lymphocytes have been demonstrated whose prime function is the regulation of the other cells of the immune system. Studies with monoclonal antibodies have shown that a similar system operates in man (Reinherz & Schlossman 1981). Any foreign antigen entering the body is processed initially by macrophages and presented to the regulatory T-lymphocytes. The precise interactions of the various sub-populations of regulatory lymphocytes are not fully understood; however, after contact with the initial regulator T-cells (T_R, also called inducer T-cells), populations of helper and suppresor T-lymphocytes develop. These cells have opposing actions, and the net balance of their effects determines the magnitude of response by the effector cells (B-lymphocytes/ plasma cells, delayed hypersensitivity T cells, and cytotoxic T cells). For humoral immune responses, the regulatory cells interact with the B-lymphocyte which differentiates into a plasma cell and secretes antibody. For cell-mediated immune responses the regulatory lymphocytes interact with other T-lymphocyte sub-populations which then act either as effector cells in their own right or recruit macrophages to produce the ultimate response.

Thus a considerable number of different cell types are involved in the generation of an immune response, and consequently there are several stages at which immune deviation may occur. The initial processing of the antigen by the macrophage may be affected by competition from other antigens or by activation of the macrophages by bacteria and various bacterial products. Alteration of the mobilisation of macrophages from the bone marrow and their trafficking to the site of infection will also alter the magnitude of the immune response. This latter effect is also applicable to other cells of the immune system. Antigenic competition may also occur at various other points in the pathway, and nonspecific activation may also occur with other cell populations, such as the effector lymphocytes, e.g. polyclonal activation of B-lymphocytes by bacterial endotoxin and activation of T-lymphocytes by viruses. Finally, nonspecific induction of suppressor cells may occur. This is a relatively common finding in microbially-induced immunosuppression.

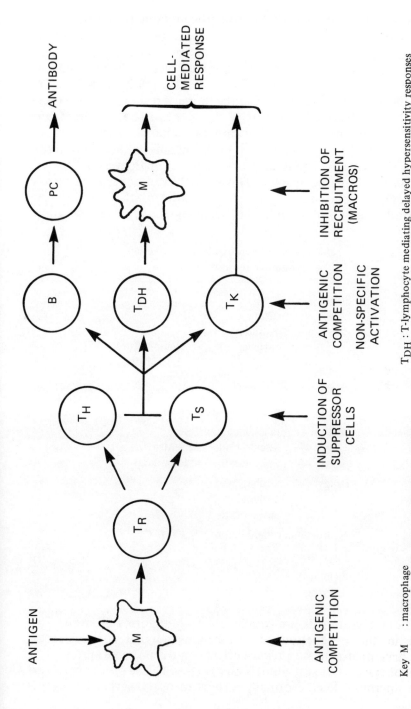

Fig. 1 – Schematic representation of the immunoregulatory network showing the pathways involved in the generation of immune responses and some of the possible points of intervention where immune deviation may occur.

Key M   : macrophage
     T_R : regulator T-lymphocyte (inducer T-lymphocyte)
     T_H : helper T-lymphocyte
     T_S : suppressor T-lymphocyte

     T_{DH} : T-lymphocyte mediating delayed hypersensitivity responses
     T_K : cytotoxic T-lymphocyte (killer cell)
     B   : B-lymphocyte
     PC   : plasma cell

Non-microbial factors known to affect the immune responses

Microorganisms are probably the major cause of variability in immunological experiments. However, non-microbial factors also play an important role. The main non-microbial factors known to affect immune responsiveness are listed in Table 1. In animals with latent infections, these factors may affect the immune response to an experimental antigen in two ways. Firstly the agent will have a direct (and possibly predictable) effect on the immune system. This will alter the animal's control over any resident microorganisms, and may result in activation of any latent infection which will then exert its own effect on the immune system. This secondary effect will be totally unpredictable, being dependent on the nature of the latent microorganism, the ability of the animal to overcome the acute exacerbation, etc.

Table 1 — Non-microbial factors affecting
immune responsiveness

Stress	—	travel	
	—	caging	
	—	handling	
	—	environment	— temperature
			— humidity
			— noise
			— lighting
	—	experimental procedures	
Diet	—	protein content	
	—	essential trace elements	
	—	poly-unsaturated fatty acids	
Drugs	—	antibacterial	
	—	antiviral	
	—	antiparasitic	
Nonspecific inflammation			
Tumours			
Pregnancy			

Laboratory animals are exposed to various forms of stress. This results in the production of endogenous adrenal corticosteroids which have profound suppressive effects on the immune system. The effects of travel stress on animals vary greatly. This is probably related to the microbial load. Normally a short recovery period (7 days) is sufficient to overcome the immediate direct effects of travel stress. However, if a latent infection is activated, as has been observed with respiratory tract infections in rabbits, this may require a much longer recovery period and treatment with antibiotics. The development of SPF animals has reduced this problem to a considerable extent, but there is still a need for improvement in transportation methods.

Caging density and environmental conditions are very important since these will exert an influence throughout the course of the experiment. As will be mentioned in more detail in specific examples, high cage density, handling, movement, and proximity of other animals have all been shown to generate stress of sufficient magnitude to suppress adjuvant arthritis, an immunologically based model of arthritis in rats. Although most reports associate stress with immunosuppression, certain stress situations may produce immuno-stimulation (Amkraut *et al.* 1971). Furthermore, Monjan & Collector (1977) found that whereas short-term exposure to sound-stress produced immunosuppression which was associated with increased plasma cortisol levels, long-term exposure to sound produced immunostimulation. This latter effect was unrelated to plasma cortisol levels but may be related to alterations in the levels of other hormones.

It has long been known that dietary factors influence immuno-logical responses. The most obvious problem of microbial contamination of diets has been alleviated to a certain extent by strict quality control procedures, although even very small levels of bacterial products, such as endotoxins, may influence responses (see later). Immunosuppression due to protein calorie malnutrition is unlkely with unrestricted feeding on modern diets; however, the protein content of the diet should be considered if restricted feeding is to be used. The level of trace elements such as magnesium, copper, and zinc should also be considered since these have been shown to be required for normal immune function (West 1980), and certain pelleted diets lack sufficient levels of these three elements. Finally, polyunsaturated fatty acids have been shown to influence immune responsiveness (reviewed by Floersheim 1979). Therefore, in view of the fact that many dietary factors may affect immunological experiments, it would be wise for users and breeders to rationalise on a single commonly acceptable diet.

In addition to drugs used therapeutically to modify immune responses, many drugs are known to influence the immune system. These include certain antimicrobial drugs (Floersheim 1979), which precludes their use for the treatment of infections occurring during long-term studies. However, their use prior to the beginning of an experiment may be acceptable provided a sufficient recovery period is given.

The presence of acute non-immunological inflammation can also influence immune responsiveness and host resistance against pathogens. For example inflammation induced in mice by sub-cutaneous injection of magnesium silicate particle increased the host resistance to *Schistosoma mansoni, Candida albicans, Plasmodium berghei, Listeria monocytogenes, Salmonella typhimurium,* and Lewis carcinoma (Fauve *et al.* 1981). Similarly Giroud *et al.* 1981) showed that an inflammatory response induced with dextran or calcium pyrophosphate protected mice against *Klebsiella pneumoniae* and *Trypanosoma cruzi.* Other factors known to affect immune responses include the presence of tumours (Ting *et al.* 1977) and pregnancy (Purtilo *et al.* 1972), both of which, in general, produce immunosuppression.

MICROORGANISMS KNOWN TO AFFECT THE IMMUNE RESPONSE

Bacteria

Many bacteria are capable of modifying the immune response of an animal to an unrelated experimental antigen. This may result in stimulation or suppression of either cell-mediated or humoral responses or both. Moreover, stimulation of humoral responses and suppression of cell-mediated immune responses may be observed and vice versa. Whether infection with any particular bacterium produces suppression or stimulation of any particular part of the immune system is dependent on many factors including the nature of the bacterium, the time of the infection relative to presentation of the experimental antigen, and the dose and route of administration of bacterium and experimental antigen. This subject has been reviewed in detail by Schwab (1975) and Floersheim (1979). I therefore propose to discuss a few selected examples to illustrate some of the mechanisms involved in bacterial immunomodulation.

The main bacteria known to modify immune responses are listed in Table 2. Group A Streptococci generally bring about a reduction in antibody production (Malakian & Schwab 1968). Various mechanisms of action have been proposed. These include inhibition of lymphocyte and granulocyte maturation from bone marrow stem cells (Gaumer and Schwab 1972), stimulation of suppressor T-cells (Schwab 1975), and inhibition of phagocytosis and antigen processing by macrophages (Hanna & Watson 1968).

Corynebacterium parvum generally stimulates immune responses

Table 2 – Bacteria and bacterial products known to modify immune responses in experimental animals and man.

Agent	Species
Group A Streptococcus – Membrane-associated suppressant	Mouse
– Pyrogenic exotoxin	Rabbit
– Techoic acid	Mouse
Corynebacterium parvum	Mouse
Vibrio cholera enterotoxin	Mouse
Pseudomonas aeruginosa	Mouse, guinea-pig, rat
Bordetella pertussis	Mouse, guinea-pig
Eschericia coli	Mouse
Klebsiella pneumoniae	Mouse
Salmonella typhimurium	Rat
Salmonella typhi	Guinea-pig
Salmonella paratyphi	Guinea-pig
Mycoplasma	Rat
Mycobacteria	Rat, guinea-pig, human
Bacterial enzymes – L-Asparaginase	Mouse, human
– L-Glutaminase	Human
– Ribonuclease	Mouse

Adapted form Schwab (1975) and Floersheim (1979).

when given prior to the experimental antigen, but suppresses the response if given after antigen. Increases in immunity to transplanted tumours (Woodruff *et al.* 1972), *Brucella abortus* and *Bordetella pertussis* infections (Adlam *et al.* 1972), and protozoal infections (Nussensweig 1967) have all been reported with *C. parvum*. Conversely, responsiveness to PHA, mixed lymphocyte reactions, and graft v. host responses have been shown to be suppressed after *C. parvum* treatment (Scott 1972), as have responses to *Salmonella enteritidis* (Collins & Scott 1974) and *Trichinella spiralis* (Ruitenberg & Steerenberg 1973). These effects of *C. parvum* may be mediated via an effect on macrophage function altering macrophage-T-cell interaction (Howard *et al.* 1973) or alternatively through activation of suppressor cells (Floersheim 1979).

The immunomodulatory actions of many bacteria may be mediated through endotoxin, of which the active component is probably lipid A. As with *C. parvum,* endotoxin may either suppress or enhance immune responses (antibody formation) depending on the dose, route, and timing of administration of the endotoxin and antigen. However, in contrast to *C. parvum,* when administered before antigen, endotoxin suppressed antibody production, whereas when administered with or after antigen, enhancement was obtained (Johnson *et al.* 1977, Franzl & McMaster 1968). The mechanism of action seems to be associated with lymphocytotoxicity since mice given endotoxin showed extensive depletion of lymphocytes in the spleen and lymph nodes (McMaster & Franzl 1968). If antigen was given at the same time as endotoxin, the lymphoid tissue recovered cellularity after 24 h with an increased number of stimulated lymphocytes, which would explain the immunostimulation observed under these conditions. This lymphocytotoxic effect of endotoxin may be due to release of adrenal hormones and their subsequent effect on T-cells (Rowlands *et al.* 1965). Endotoxin has an additional stimulatory effect on B-lympocytes (Goodman & Weigle 1981) possibly mediated via activation of the alternative complement pathway (Dukor *et al.* 1974). Although endotoxin primarily interferes with antibody responses, suppression of cell-mediated immune responses has also been reported (Floersheim & Szeszak 1972). This is probably mediated through an effect on lymphocyte distribution.

In conclusion, many bacteria are capable of modifying the immune responsiveness of experimental animals in either a suppressive or stimulatory manner. This may be achieved through a variety of mechanisms, except antigenic competition which seemed unlikely to account for bacterial immunosuppression (Quagliata & Taranta 1972). One of the principal concerns arising from the foregoing comments in this section is that bacterial products are as effective as the living microorganism at altering the immune system. Therefore sterilisation of materials such as cages, bedding, diet, etc. by irradiation or autoclaving will not completely eliminate bacterial induced immunomodification although it will reduce it to a certain extent by elimination of live organisms.

Viruses
The suppression of immunological responses in man by viruses has been well documented (Notkins *et al.* 1970, Kantor 1975), and a similar situation occurs in laboratory animals (Notkins *et al.* 1970, Bro-Jorgensen 1978). Virus infection nearly always produces immunosuppression, and this often results in an increased incidence of bacterial superinfection. However, immunostimulation has been observed with some viruses.

Table 3 illustrates the broad spectrum of viruses known to modify immunological responsiveness. Either humoral or cell-mediated

Table 3 – Viruses known to modify the immune response.

Infecting virus	Species
Gross leukaemia	Mouse
Friend leukaemia	Mouse
Moloney leukaemia	Rat, mouse
Rauscher leukaemia	Mouse
Avian leukosis	Chicken
Marek's disease	Chicken
Lymphocytic choriomeningitis	Mouse
M–P virus	Mouse
Junin	Guinea-pig
Mouse cytomegalovirus	Mouse
Aleutian mink disease	Mink
Newcastle disease	Rabbit
Lactic dehydrogenase	Mouse
Venezuelan equine encephalitis	Mouse, guinea-pig
Ectromelia	Mouse
Measles	Human
Influenza	Human
Chicken pox	Human
Polio	Human
Rubella	Human
Hepatitis	Human
Epstein–Barr virus	Human
Mumps	Human
Yellow fever	Human
Dengue	Human
Sandfly fever	Human

Adapted from Notkins *et al.* (1970) and Kantor (1975).

immunity, or both, may be affected by virus infection, as may reticuloendothelial function. Various mechanisms have been proposed for virus-induced immunomodulation. Measles virus suppresses cell-mediated immune responses probably by inhibition of leucocyte migration (Nordal *et al.* 1975), although nonspecific activation of T-lymphocytes may also play a role (Valdimarsson *et al.* 1975). Cell-mediated immune responsiveness is also suppressed by Epstein–Barr virus (Mangi *et al.* 1975), which may be due to depression of chemotactic responsiveness of monocytes (Kleinerman *et al.* 1975). In addition E–B virus can produce polyclonal B-cell activation (Bardwick *et al*. 1980) as can many other microorganisms and their products (Goodman & Weigle 1981), thereby altering antibody production. Acute E–B virus infection in man has also been shown to be associated with activation of suppressor T-cells capable of inhibiting both cell-mediated and humoral immunity (Reinherz *et al*. 1980).

The actions of Friend Leukaemia virus on the immune system of mice have been reviewed in detail by Friedman & Specter (1981). Marked alterations in the immune response became evident early after infection. The virus mainly influenced B-lymphocytes and their precursors, resulting in a suppression of antibody production (particularly IgM), but T-lymphocytes also seemed to be affected late in the leukaemic process. The mechanism for these effects is probably viral leukaemogenesis, although an effect on macrophages may also be involved.

Parasites

In addition to bacteria and viruses, protozoan and metazoan parasites can modify host immune responses. *Plasmodium berghei* diminishes antibody responses in mice without affecting cell-mediated immune responses such as skin graft rejection and contact sensitivity to picryl chloride or oxazolone (Greenwood *et al*. 1971). The mechanism of this suppression of antibody production seems to be an alteration of macrophage function. Trypanosomes also suppress antibody production in experimental animals (Hudson *et al*. 1976) and suppress both humoral and cell-mediated immunity in man (Greenwood *et al*. 1973). Various mechanisms have been proposed. These include polyclonal B-cell stimulation, complement activation, and the generation of free fatty acids by the parasite (Assoku *et al*. 1977) as well as the induction of suppressor T-cells (Jayawardena & Waksman 1977). Toxoplasma and syphilis infections also produce immunosuppression, but the mechanisms are unknown.

Metazoan parasites can also cause immunosuppression. *Trichinella spiralis* infection of mice reduced antibody responses (Faubert & Tanner 1971) possibly through induction of suppressor T-cells (Barriga 1978). The presence of viable organisms was required for this effect. Skin graft rejection was also suppressed by *T. spiralis* (Chernyakhovskaya *et al*. 1972).

The difficulty in interpretation of results under conditions such as these is illustrated by the observation that infection of mice with *T. spiralis* either before or after sensitisation with viable BCG increased the delayed hypersensitivity responsiveness to tuberculin. This is probably due to the reduction in antibody production allowing greater multiplication of the BCG which led to increased antigen stimulus and greater delayed hypersensitivity (Cypress *et al*. 1974).

Other metazoan parasites known to have immunosuppressive effects include *Demodex canis* (Corbett *et al*. 1975) and *Nippostrongylus brasiliensis* (Keller *et al*. 1971).

Implications

From the preceding sections it can be seen that any infection is likely to affect the results of immunological experiments, This may manifest itself in either stimulation or suppression at any one of several stages in the immune pathway. Moreover, with any one microorganism different mechanisms of immunomodulation may occur at different stages of the infection. The nature and magnitude of microbial-induced immunomodulation is dependent on many factors including the level of infection, the dose of experimental antigen under consideration, and its route of administration, and the timing of antigen administration relative to infection. Therefore, the results obtained from immunological experiments performed on conventional animals, in which there exists multiple sub-clinical infections, are open to question. The most obvious solution is the removal of as many microorganisms as possible from the animals at the breeding stage and the maintenance of these animals in a sterile controlled environment throughout the course of the experiment. This will be discussed fully later.

Deviation of immune responsiveness, either by microbial or non-microbial factors, is likely to manifest itself in many ways. In the most extreme situation death of the animals will result from severe infection, especially where the use of antibiotics is prohibited by the nature of the experiment. With sub-lethal or sub-clinical infections, or in the case of non-microbial factors, a general reduction (or elevation) of immune responsiveness may be seen in an animal colony; but much more of a problem is variability in responsiveness between different groups of animals or between different animals within a group. A further problem is variation in responsiveness of control animals from day to day or from week to week (baseline fluctuation).

Many immunological experiments involve the investigation of cellular function either *in vitro* or after adoptive transfer to a recipient (either normal or, more often X-irradiated). In these situations, microbial infection of the donor animal may affect the number of cells in the particular organ (e.g. thymus, spleen, lymph nodes, bone marrow, blood) or body cavity (e.g. peritoneum, pleural cavity) under investigation by alteration of the multiplication rate and distribution of the cells. Furthermore, the activation state of these cells may also be affected. In adoptive transfer studies to either X-irradiated or thymectomised animals, transfer of microorganisms to the compromised recipient could markedly affect the functions of the transferred cells.

These points will be illustrated in more detail in the specific examples described in the following section.

SPECIFIC EXAMPLES

In vitro studies of macrophage function

One of the experimental systems currently in use in our laboratory involves the investigation of mouse macrophage functions. Peritoneal macrophages are plated onto Petri dishes, and the adherent cells challenged with various stimuli. Following pinocytosis/phagocytosis of the stimulus by the macrophages, the cells become stimulated and secrete a variety of products into the culture medium. During this sequence of events, various parameters may be measured, including phagocytosis rate, intracellular metabolic events such as hexose monophosphate shunt activation and increased protein synthesis, and secretion of enzymes and other soluble mediators into the culture medium.

Alterations in the peritoneal cell population used for this type of study may occur in various ways as a result of infection. Localised infections in other sites may stimulate migration of the cells out of the peritoneal cavity which may then become repopulated with immature monocytes or promonocytes. Conversely, the number of macrophages within the peritoneal cavity may be increased by infection within the peritoneum. In this instance a proportion of the peritoneal cells will be committed to combating the infection and hence unavailable for activation *in vitro* during the experiment, thus producing a reduction in the total cellular activity. Furthermore, the presence of a peritoneal infection will also stimulate infiltration of lymphocytes and polymorphonuclear leucocytes into the peritoneal cavity, further altering the cell count and proportion of macrophages available for activation *in vitro*. Perhaps a more important consequence of peritoneal infection is the alteration of the activation state of the macrophages. Microorganisms may activate macrophages either directly or indirectly through interaction with sensitised lymphocytes which secrete lymphokines which in turn stimulate the macrophage. Preactivation (or stimulation) of the macrophages *in vivo* will render them refractory to subsequent *in vitro* stimulation.

Examples of this process include infection of the peritoneal cavity with small numbers of intestinal flagellates, e.g. Hexamita or

Giardia, which should not cross the intestinal wall under normal circumstances, but may cross in the presence of moderate to heavy infestation with *Syphacia obvelata*. In our experience, in such circumstances even very low levels of microbial contamination of the peritoneal cavity can drastically alter the functional status of the resident peritoneal macrophages.

Many other *in vitro* culture systems may be affected in a similar way by either localised or generalised infections. These include lymphocyte transformation studies and mixed lymphocyte reactions (which utilise peripheral blood leukocytes, thymus cells, lymph node cells, spleen cells, and bone marrow cells), plaque-forming cell studies which employ spleen cells, and leucocyte/macrophage chemotaxis/ chemokinesis studies which utilise cells from the peripheral blood or peritoneum mainly.

In vivo studies of cell-mediated immunity

The delayed contact hypersensitivity response to oxazolone in mice is a commonly used model of cell-mediated immune responses. Animals are sensitised by painting oxazolone on to the abdomen and challenged 3-7 days later with a similar application of a low dose of oxazolone to the ear. The reaction may be quantitated either radio-metrically or by measurement of ear thickness. With conventional outbred mice considerable variation in the response to oxazolone was observed both between different animals at any one time and from week to week. The use of category three inbred mice kept under conventional conditions dramatically decreased the intra-group varia-tion, although there was still significant baseline variation in the responses of untreated animals from week to week. We therefore compared the responsiveness of these animals kept under conventional conditions with that of identical animals (from the same batch) kept in a laminar flow cabinet. The results are shown in Fig. 2. Animals kept in the normal animal room showed an increase in responsiveness after two weeks in this environment, presumably owing to immuno-stimulation by antigens (microorganisms or microbial products) presented to the animals prior to the administration of oxazolone. This was followed by suppression of responsiveness which may have been due to further microbial challenge or merely a reflection of the development of an infection resulting from the earlier challenge. Animals kept in the laminar flow cabinet showed a slight increase in responsiveness at two weeks, but subsequent responses were similar to the initial response. The results of this preliminary experiment with category three animals under far from ideal conditions has shown that week to week baseline variations can be minimised by keeping

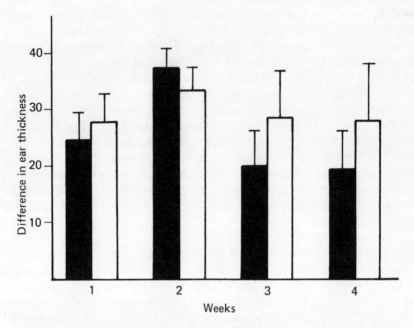

Fig. 2 – Delayed hypersensitivity responses to oxazolone in category three Balb/c mice kept in an uncontrolled environment as compared to identical animals maintained in a laminar flow cabinet. Animals were kept for 1–4 weeks then sensitised with oxazolone and challenged 7 days later. Each bar represents the mean ± SD of 10 animals. Each experiment was performed on a separate group of animals.

Open bars: animals kept in laminar flow cabinet.

animals in a sterile environment, thereby minimising the variation in microbial flora within the animals.

Rat adjuvant arthritis

This well-characterised model of acute/chronic polyarthritis is induced by intradermal injection of heat-killed *Mycobacterium tuberculosis* in mineral oil into rats (Pearson 1964, Owen 1980). The development of the arthritis is dependent on immunological responsiveness to the mycobacterium, particularly at the T-cell level (Kaysahima *et al.* 1978). The development of the arthritis is affected by many factors including diet, stress, and infection. West (1980) has studied the effects of dietary metal deficiency on the development of adjuvant arthritis and dextran anaphylactoid reactions in rats. The animals were fed the diet for two weeks, injected with adjuvant and then left for three weeks on the deficient diet. Dextran was injected both at 10 and 20 days after adjuvant. A deficiency of copper, magnesium, or zinc, or in the three elements together inhibited the development of adjuvant arthritis, although a deficiency of both copper and magnesium had no such effect. The dextran anaphylactoid reaction was inhibited only by a magnesium deficiency. These inhibitions were observed with both high-carbohydrate and high-protein diets. These results suggest that different results will be obtained with different commercial diets, and therefore the optimum diet must be chosen for immunological studies.

The effects of stress on the development of adjuvant arthritis has been studied by several workers. Overcrowding stress reduced the severity of the disease (Sofia 1980) although an increase in the disease severity has been found with stress induced by mixed-sex group housing at male: female ratios $\geqslant 1$ (Amkraut *et al.* 1971). Overcrowding stress has also been found to reduce antibody responses to flagellar antigens in rats (Solomon 1969). The incidence and severity of collagen-induced arthritis in rats has also been shown to be markedly reduced by transportation and handling (transfer to a different cage for 10 min every six hours) and exposure to a cat (Rodgers *et al.* 1980). Stress induced by electric shock treatment has also been shown to reduce lymphocyte function in rats (Keller *et al.* 1981). Therefore, variations in stress levels during immunological experiments are bound to bring about marked alterations in the results.

Finally, the effects of infection on the incidence and severity of adjuvant arthritis have been investigated by Kohashi *et al.* (1979) whose results are summarised in Table 4. Germ-free F344 rats

Table 4 – **Susceptibility to adjuvant arthritis in germ-free, specific pathogen free, and conventional rats.**

		Inducing antigen			
		M. Bovis		Peptidoglycan	
Strain		Incidence	Severity	Incidence	Severity
F344	GF	6/6	11.8	8/8	11.8
	SPF	4/6	5.3	2/8	3.5
	CV	2/10	8.0	0/8	0
Lewis	CV	6/6	15.9	8/8	14.2

From Kohashi *et al.* (1979).

developed severe arthritis with 100% incidence after injection of either heat-killed *Mycobacterium bovis* or *Staphylococcus epidermidis* peptidoglycan. Conventional F344 rats developed less severe arthritis with *M. Bovis* and produced no response to the peptidoglycan, whereas SPF animals showed an intermediate susceptibility. Interestingly, conventional Lewis rats produced a severe arthritis with 100% incidence. These results show that bacterial flora is not necessary for the induction of adjuvant arthritis and that it has a suppressive effect on the development of the disease in SPF and conventional F344 rats. This suppression may be due to the bacterial flora acting as a stimulus for induction of cell-mediated immunity to ubiquitous bacterial peptidoglycans and a consequent generation of suppressor cells. Similarly, there have been anecdotal reports of a suppression of responsiveness to adjuvant in rats with chronic respiratory disease.

Rabbit monoarticular arthritis

The rabbit model of arthritis developed by Dumonde & Glynn (1962) and modified by Consden *et al.* (1971) is a chronic self-perpetuating monoarticular arthritis model. It is induced by sensitisation of rabbits to a soluble protein such as ovalbumin, followed by injection of ovalbumin into one knee joint. The development of the arthritis is dependent on both humoral and cell-mediated immune responses to the antigen. There is probably a reasonable level of stress associated with these experimental procedures, e.g. immunisation, the presence of the chronic arthritis, and daily dosing by gastric intubation (for up to ten weeks) which may predispose the animals to infection.

In my experience, the principal problem from infection occurring in this experimental model is death of the animals during the experiment, although the presence of chronic infection may also result in immune deviation and consequently variable or misleading results. The first problem we encounter is diarrhoea and death of animals within a fortnight of delivery from the breeder. This may be due to change of diet but may also be due to proliferation of gut flora due to travel stress-induced immunosuppression. When this initial acute attack has been overcome, gastro-intestinal disturbances do not generally present a problem throughout the remainder of the experiment, although some mild cases of diarrhoea are sometimes encountered. However, later on during the experiment we have encountered severe bronchopneumonia. This usually occurs midway through the ten-week dosing period and is generally due to pasteurella, although secondary infection often occurs. The incidence of this infection seems to be unrelated to the environment, and is more likely to be due to the level of latent pulmonary infection which becomes activated owing to stress associated with the experimental procedures.

In this situation, the use of immunosuppressive drugs such as corticosteroids or cyclophosphamide may exacerbate the infection dramatically. Chronic respiratory infection such as this may produce immune deviation, as well as resulting in death of the animal. We have observed a diminution of antibody responses during the onset of chronic respiratory infection in rabbits, and in cases where the animals have been treated with antibiotics and recovered, the antibody levels have returned to pre-infection levels. Changing to a higher category of animals has alleviated this problem to a major extent.

Therefore for long-term studies such as these it is imperative to use animals that are free from latent infection. In our experience high-grade conventional animals maintained under optimal environmental conditions do not present many problems; but, ideally, SPF animals should be considered if these are available.

DISCUSSION AND RECOMMENDATIONS

From the preceding sections, it is obvious that various factors may influence immune responsiveness, and of these, microbial infection appears to be the most important. Furthermore, the non-microbial agents probably exert their main effect on immune responsiveness indirectly through activation of latent infections. The most obvious solution to this problem would be to use germ-free animals. However, germ-free animals do not produce a normal immune response to many antigens; for example germ-free mice produce very weak delayed hypersensitivity responses to sheep erythrocytes (MacDonald & Carter 1979) and tuberculin (Ueda 1975), and spleen cells from germ-free mice produce abnormally high responses to mitogens *in vitro* (McGhee *et al.* 1980). Macrophage function is also impaired in germ-free rats (Jungi & McGregor 1978). Furthermore the 'normal' NK (natural killer) activity of animals is probably dependent on naturally acquired infection (Clark *et al.* 1979). Therefore the normal regulation of immune responsiveness within an animal requires the presence of gut microbial flora.

For most immunological studies, therefore, inbred SPF animals with a restricted gut microbial flora are probably the best compromise. These may best be produced by specific repopulation of germ-free animals, although it would be difficult to decide upon the composition of the microbial cocktail used for repopulation in order to obtain a 'normal' immune response profile. Nevertheless, the result must be animals with a minimal microbial flora.

Different types of experiment will require different grades of animal. For instance, in some studies it may be desirable to use conventional outbred animals in order to mimic as closely as possible the human situation. However, in our experience the variability associated with the use of outbred animals is too great to determine subtle effects of drugs on the immune response, and inbred animals have to be used. In the other extreme, germ-free animals may be required, e.g. congenitally athymic mice have to be kept under germ-free conditions. Similarly some immunopharmacologists use cytotoxic drugs such as cyclophosphamide and methotrexate to deplete certain lymphocyte subpopulations. Under these circumstances activation of latent infections can occur; for example Tyzzer's disease may be activated by cyclophosphamide treatment, in a similar manner to its activation by high doses of prednisolone (Fries 1979). High-grade SPF animals might be suitable for this type of investigation, depending on the nature of the residual microbial flora, but it is quite likely that depletion of selected lymphocyte populations would allow uncontrolled growth of the gut flora with a consequent deviation of immune responsiveness. This may easily be checked by treatment of such animals with immunosuppressants (possibly a combination of a corticosteroid and a cytotoxic agent such as cyclophosphamide) and observation of the activation of any latent infection. Other animals which are highly susceptible to infection include the autoimmune mouse strains NZB/W, BXSB, and MRL/L. In our experience relatively minor forms of stress can activate latent Tyzzer's disease in NZB/W mice. Therefore such animals must be bred to SPF standards and barrier-maintained.

Considerable progress has been made in breeding animals to a high-grade SPF standard, although category four animals may need to be improved for immunological studies. Having produced a stable SPF colony it is imperative to maintain the stability of the microbial flora in the animals during transit to the user and throughout the period of experimental use. This will require a good dialogue between the breeder and user who in my opinion should barrier-maintain the animals throughout the course of the experiment, provided that this is technically feasible. Ideally the breeder and user should maintain the animals under identical environmental conditions (temperature, humidity), using the same diet and bedding. We must also seek ways of improving the transport of animals so that they can be transported in a sterile environment with minimum stress. Finally, the breeder and user must devise a suitable microbiological monitoring system to monitor the stability of the resident microbial flora in the animals and any contamination of the barrier facility.

In conclusion, in my opinion the best compromise for most immunological studies is a laboratory animal with a defined microbial flora which must not be allowed to vary or increase above a minimal level. The achievement of this goal will require cooperation between the breeders and users to ensure that animals are bred to an appropriate microbiological standard and maintained under optimum conditions throughout their use.

ACKNOWLEDGEMENTS

I am most grateful to my colleagues Dr D. J. Bowen and Mr D. G. Webber for most helpful discussion and for performing the experiment shown in Fig. 2.

REFERENCES

Adlam, C., Broughton, E. S. & Scott, M. T. (1972). *Nature* (New Biol.) **235**, 219.

Amkraut, A. A., Solomon, G. F. & Kraemer, H. C. (1971). *Psychosomatic Medicine* **33**, 203.

Assoku, R. K. G., Tizzard, I. R. & Nielsen, K. H. (1977). *Lancet* **2**, 956.

Bardwick, P. A., Bluestein, H. G., Zvaifler, N. J., Depper, J. M. & Seegmiller, J. E. (1980). *Arthr. and Rheum.* **23**, 626.

Barriga, O. O. (1978). *Immunology* **34**, 167.

Bro-Jorgensen, K. (1978). *Adv. Virus Research* **22**, 327.

Cantor, H. & Boyse, E. A. (1977). *Contemp. Top. Immunobiol.* **7**, 47.

Chernyakhovskaya, I. Y., Shaghijan, J. S., Slavina, E. G. & Svet-Moldavsky, G. J. (1972). *Rev. Eur. Etud. Clin. Biol.* **17**, 395.

Clark, E. A., Russell, P. H., Egghart, M. & Morton, M. A. (1979). *Int. J. Cancer.* **24**, 688.

Collins, F. M. & Scott, M. T. (1974). *Infect. Immun.* **9**, 863.

Consden, R., Doble, A., Glynn, L. E. & Nind, A. P. (1971). *Ann. Rheum. Dis.* **30**, 307.

Corbett, R., Bauks, K., Hinrichs, D. & Bell, T. (1975). *Transplant. Proc.* **7**, 555.

Cypress, R. H., Molinari, J. A., Ebersole, J. L. & Lubiniecki, A. S. (1974). *Infect. Immun.* **10**, 107.

Dukor, P., Shumann, G., Gisler, R., Dierich, M., Konig, W., Hadding, U. & Bitter-Suermann, D. (1974). *J. Exp. Med.* **139**, 337.

Dumonde, D. C. & Glynn, L. E. (1962). *Brit. J. Exp. Path.* **43**, 373.

Dutton, R. W. (1980). *Fed. Proc.* **39**, 3109.

Eardley, D. D. (1980). *Fed. Proc.* **39**. 3114.

Faubert, G. & Tanner, C. E. (1971). *Exp. Parasit.* **30**, 120.

Fauve, R. M., Hevin, M. B. & Fontan, E. (1981). In *Advances in immunopharmacology.* Eds. Hadden, J., Chedid, L., Mullen, P. & Spreafico, F., Pergamon Press, p. 245.

Floersheim, G. L. (1979). In *Drugs and immune responsiveness.* Eds. Turk, J. L. & Parker, D., MacMillan Press, p. 1.

Floersheim, G. L. & Szeszak, J. J. (1972). *Agents and Actions* **2**, 150.

Franzl, R. E. & McMaster, P. D. (1968). *J. Exp. Med.* **127**, 1087.

Friedman, H. & Specter, S. (1981). In *Advances in immunopharmacology.* Eds. Hadden, J., Chedid, L., Mullen, P. & Spreafico, F., Pergamon Press, p. 91.

Fries, A. S. (1979). *Lab. Animals* **13**, 143.

Gaumer, H. R. & Schwab, J. H. (1972). *Cell. Immunol.* **4**, 394.

Giroud, J. P., Florentin, I., Pelletier, M. & Nolibé, D. (1981). In *Advances in immunopharmacology.* Eds. Hadden, J., Chedid, L., Mullen, P. & Spreafico, F., Pergamon Press, p. 249.

Goodman, M. G. & Weigle, W. O. (1981). *Immunology Today* **March**, 54.

Greenwood, B. M., Playfair, J. H. L. & Torrigiani, G. (1971). *Clin. Exp. Immunol.* **8**, 467.

Greenwood, B. M., Whittle, H. C. & Molyneux, D. H. (1973). *Trans. R. Soc. Trop. Med. Hyg.* **67**, 846.

Hanna, E. E. & Watson, D. W. (1968). *Infect. Immun.* **7**, 1009.

Howard, J. G., Christian, G. H. & Scott, M. T. (1973). *Cell. Immunol.* **7**, 290.

Hudson, K. M., Byner, C., Freeman, J. & Terry, R. J. (1976). *Nature* **264**, 256.

Jayawardena, A. N. & Waksman, B. H. (1977). *Nature* **265**, 539.

Johnson, A. G., Jacobs, A., Abrams, G. & Merrit, K. (1967). In *Germinal centres in immune response.* Eds. Cottier, H., Odortchenko, N. D., Schindler, R. & Congden, C. C., Springer-Verlag, p. 214.

Jungi, T. W. & McGregor, D. D. (1978). *Infect. Immun.* **19**, 553.

Kantor, F. S. (1975). *N. Engl. J. Med.* **292**, 629.

Kayashima, K., Koga, T. & Onue, K. (1978). *J. Immunol.* **120**, 1127.

Keller, R., Ogilvie, R. M. & Simpson, E. (1971). *Lancet* **1**, 678.

Keller, S. E., Weiss, J. M., Schleifer, S. J., Miller, N. E. & Stein, M. (1981). *Science* **213**, 1397.

Kleinerman, E. S., Synderman, R. & Daniels, C. A. (1975). *Lancet* **2**, 1063.

Kohashi, O., Kuwata, J., Umehara, K., Uemura, F., Takahashi, T. & Ozawa, A. (1979). *Inject. Immun.* **26**, 791.

MacDonald, T. T. & Carter, P. B. (1979). *J. Immunol.* **122**, 2624.

Malakian, A. H. & Schwab, J. H. (1968). *Science* **159**, 880.

Mangi, R. J., Niederman, J. C. & Kelleher, J. E. Jr. (1975). *N. Engl. J. Med.* **291**, 1149.

McGee, J. R., Kiyono, H., Michalek, S. M., Babb, J. L., Rosenstreich, D. L. & Mergenhagen, S. E. (1980). *J. Immunol.* **124**, 1603.

McMaster, P. D. & Franzl, R. E. (1968). *J. Exp. Med.* **127**, 1109.

Monjan, A. A. & Collector, M. I. (1977). *Science* **196**, 307.

Nordal, H. J., Froland, S. S., Vandvik, B. & Norby, E. (1975). *Lancet* **2**, 1266.

Notkins, A. L., Mergenhagen, S. E. & Howard, R. J. (1970). *Ann. Rev. Microbiol.* **24**, 525.

Nussensweig, R. S. (1967). *Exp. Parasit.* **21**, 224.

Owen, R. T. (1980). *Methods and Findings in Exp. Clin. Pharmacol.* **2**, 199.

Pearson, C. M. (1964). *Arthr. and Rheum.* **7**, 80.

Purtilo, D. T., Hallgren, H. M. & Yunis, E. J. (1972). *Lancet* **1**, 769.

Quagliata, F. & Taranta, A. (1972). *Ann. Rheum. Dis.* **31**, 200.

Reinherz, E. L., O'Brein, C., Rosenthal, P. & Schlossman, S. F. (1980). *J. Immunol.* **125**, 1269.

Reinherz, E. L. & Schlossman, S. F. (1981). *Immunology Today* **April**, 69.

Rogers, M. P., Trentham, D. E., McCune, W. J., Ginsberg, B. I., Rennke, H. G., Reich, P. & David, J. R. (1980). *Arthr. and Rheum.* **23**, 1337.

Rowlands, D. T. Jr., Claman, H. N. & Kind, P. D. (1965). *Am. J. Pathol.* **46**, 165.

Ruitenberg, E. J. & Steerenberg, P. A. (1973). *Nature* (New Biol.) **242**, 149.

Schwab, J. H. (1975). *Bacteriol. Reviews* **39**, 121.

Scott, M. T. (1972). *Cell. Immunol.* **5**, 459.

Sofia, R. D. (1980). *J. Pharm. Pharmacol.* **32**, 874.

Solomon, G. F. (1969). *Int. Arch. Allergy appl. Immunol.* **35**, 97.

Swain, S. L. (1980). *Fed. Proc.* **39**, 3110.

Ting, C. C., Tsai, S. C. & Rogers, M. J. (1977). *Science* **197**, 571.

Ueda, K., Yamazaki, S. & Someya, S. (1975). *J. Reticuloendothelial Soc.* **18**, 107.

Valdimarsson, H., Agnarsdottir, G. & Lachmann, P. J. (1975). *Nature* **255**, 554.

West, G. B. (1980). *Int. Arch. Allergy appl. Immunol.* **63**, 347.

Woodruff, M. F. A., Inchley, M. P. & Dunbar, N. (1972). *Br. J. Cancer* **26**, 67.

6

Problems in the supply of healthy sheep

G. S. Dawes, **CBE**, **FRS**, The Nuffield Institute of Medical Research, Headley Way, Headington, Oxford OX3 9DS

INTRODUCTION

Research in perinatal medicine is ultimately directed towards characterising foetal health, and the normality or otherwise of growth before delivery, to ensure a smooth transition into postnatal life with the large physiological adjustments which take place at birth. Independent life involves a major transition, for which elaborate preparations are made in the endocrine functions of the foetus and in the development of physiological and immunological mechanisms.

During the past twenty years it has become apparent that in species such as man a relatively elaborate development of behavioural mechanisms occurs late in foetal life. Patterns of sleep and wakefulness are already established in the human infant born prematurely at 36 weeks' gestation. We also now recognise that foetal breathing is established prenatally, though it is episodic and not directly linked to metabolism. In the sheep, for instance, breathing movements occur only in association with low-voltage electrocortical activity characteristic of rapid eye movement sleep; these episodes are present up to 40% of the time. In the human a large fraction of each day, postnatally, is spent in rapid eye movement sleep, much greater than in adult life. Evidence has accumulated in the past five years, from many investigators all over the world, that such breathing movements prenatally are essential to the normal development of the lungs.

There is, therefore, a need for further work on animal species related to the prenatal development of these physiological systems encompassing both sophisticated aspects of central nervous function and also the hormonal developments which antedate foetal control of parturition. An account of these investigations in a number of species has been given in recent Ciba symposia (Ciba Foundation 1969, 1974, 1977, 1981a,b).

CHOICE OF SPECIES FOR RESEARCH ON FOETAL DEVELOPMENT

Now let us turn to the question of appropriate animal species for these investigations. We need pregnant animals in sufficient numbers with pregnancies accurately dated to the nearest day. Experience has shown that experiments on small animals (e.g. rats and mice) are of limited value in perinatal medicine because these species are altricial, the young are poorly developed at birth, and they are not comparable to man in that they are multiparous and with development of sleep behavioural states only postnatally. As Sir Joseph Barcroft (1947) noted many years ago, in these species the stages of development are compressed into too short a period for them to be readily discriminated. The rabbit, though larger at birth, also has a relatively short gestation. The guinea-pig looked more promising because it is precocial at birth with reasonable temperature control, relatively independent, and with a gestation period of about 65 days. Since a good method was found for identifying oestrus (Elvidge 1972) it also is more easy to breed for the purpose. Further attempts to implant indwelling catheters into the foetus have had a low degree of success, and the relatively small size of the foetus has limited its use for extensive physiological studies. Nevertheless this species is used for studies of growth retardation, induced by ligation of a uterine artery, and for consequential biochemical and endocrine investigations. There do not appear to be any great problems about its production for this purpose.

The species on which most work has been done in the past 50 years on prenatal physiology is the sheep. It has the advantage of being mature at birth, of size (about 4 kg) such that repeated blood samples may be taken and elaborate instruments implanted. The mother and the foetus withstand surgery well with rapid recovery and healing. The uterus does not contract vigorously on incision, and with experience a high degree of success can be achieved in complex antenatal preparations. This experience contrasts well with that on Rhesus monkeys, which were not surprisingly investigated because of their closer relationship with man. The success of using this species for implantation of catheters, or electrode leads *in utero*, has been low, so that most investigators have limited prenatal studies to investigations which are essential to answer directly a particular medical problem. We also have to take into account their high cost and low availability. We conclude that the only practical species for these kinds of investigations at the moment are sheep. Goats have been used, and those of my colleagues who have used them tell me they are satisfactory. Their physiological behaviour is similar to that of the sheep foetus, but they are not normally available in the quantities needed for experimental purposes. Some studies have been done, notably on the west coast of North America, using the pygmy goat, which is an attractive and useful species. The capybara (*Hydrochoerus capybara*) has also been used on a limited scale; it is satisfactory from the scientific point of view but requires elaborate precautions against escape and is expensive.

THE SHEEP AS AN ANIMAL MODEL

Experience over the past 30 years in arranging for a supply of pregnant sheep has made us aware of a large number of problems, some related to the supply of particular breeds and others related to the requirements with regard to health. Alas, we cannot subscribe to the view of James Thurber who wrote to a friend in 1937 "as far as I can make out, what you have is sheep blast ... It comes from a mixture of 'Comment' writing and whisk broom catchings ... It is really a flatulent condition of certain sheep, and this is unusual because sheep have almost no diseases. You couldn't give a sheep syphilis, for instance, or vent gleet. Sheep bleat is common enough, and I have it myself " (Thurber & Weeks 1981). So he may have had, but evidently had little direct experience of sheep although he wrote of sheep and men with imagination and wit.

Generally speaking, breeders have tried to increase the production of sheep by selecting for multiple pregnancies. From the point of view of the experimentalist twin pregnancy may or may not be an advantage, but the presence of triplets, quadruplets, or more is often disastrous. Twins are sometimes preferred when comparisons are to be made between an operated and unoperated twin, e.g. in assessing the effect of an operative procedure on lung growth, such as section of the phrenic nerves or tracheotomy. But for many purposes, and especially where the foetus is likely to be subjected to a long opera-tion for implantation of elaborate measuring devices to record blood flow or to record electrocortical activity and eye movements, or to study spinal segmental reflexes, then a single pregnancy is preferable. We therefore would prefer to have a reasonable mix of single and twin pregnancies in any one season, and in order to diagnose them we X-ray the sheep at 80–90 days' gestation.

The size and behaviour of the breed are also matters of interest.

Very large Suffolk or Hampshires are difficult to handle while some breeds, e.g. Mules, are fractious and easily upset. This is so, even when the ewes are always given a companion. And careful observation has shown that ewes that are easily disturbed are likely to give rise to unwanted sudden changes in body temperature, for instance, and large rises in plasma glucose concentrations.

DISEASES OF SHEEP AND PROBLEMS OF HUSBANDRY

Apart from care in selecting breeds there are many other problems concerning the health and bacterial flora of sheep which we have to take into account. Good management always goes back to good farm practice. Such simple measures as avoiding flocks on low-lying land in which a winter storm may bring down the snails containing the liver fluke, or good husbandry to avoid foot rot, have from time to time proved essential features in maintaining a supply of animals which will provide healthy young. At one time, many years ago, we got caught with a clostridial infection after operation because of failure to vaccinate the ewes within a reasonable time of delivery. This is essential within a few months of any operative procedure. Other diseases which we have had to consider are scrapie which is, however, late in manifestation and therefore only likely to be encountered in culled sheep at five or six years of age. Toxaemia of pregnancy, especially in severe weather, is readily avoided by maintaining an adequate food supply in late pregnancy and should not now be a cause of trouble. Mastitis can occur and is treated with antibiotics locally. These are all aspects of good husbandry which any reputable shepherd will handle adequately, together with periodic drenching for worm infestation and dip to prevent or eradicate insect infestation. There are two diseases transmissible to man which should be mentioned, one of which is readily recognised as a herpes-like infection and easily treated. Q fever is more insidious, tick-borne, and though readily diagnosed serologically, when contracted gives rise to fever in man, which can be treated effectively with antibiotics. Fortunately, human infection in this country is uncommon. We have not had experience of toxoplasmosis confirmed bacteriologically. In summary there are a large number of infectious diseases to which sheep are subject which should be minimised by good farm management, but which as every experimentalist will recognise, are not always controlled and which may be exacerbated by operative procedures. Any responsible investigator who suspects that a pregnant sheep is not sound will recognise the hazards of early parturition or foetal death, in addition to the effects of operation upon the mother.

MAINTAINING AN ADEQUATE SUPPLY
OF PREGNANT SHEEP

Finally we must consider the problem of maintaining a reasonable supply of dated pregnant sheep during the year. Experience has shown that it is not sensible to try to maintin a supply every month, both for economic reasons and because the staff need holidays and time to assess and write up their results in the summer. We now aim to provide pregnant sheep, from 90 days' gestation upwards, from September to May. This is achieved by buying ewe lambs at appropriate times of the year, wintering them as required, and inducing synchronised oestrus by implantation of vaginal tampons impregnated with progesterone for fourteen days, followed by injection of PMS (Pregnant Mare's Serum) as required. They are then run in small numbers with rams of proven potency, and mating is identified from the raddle marks. Pregnancy can be confirmed by measurement of maternal plasma progesterone within two weeks, but this is liable to be expensive.

Otherwise the use of an ultrasound probe, inserted rectally to identify the Doppler signals reflected from blood flow in the enlarged uterine arteries, is being explored. The foetal heart-beat is not readily detected by ultrasound for several weeks later. Early identification of non-pregnant ewes is essential so that they can be recycled. The logistics of this operation are complicated by the lower success rate which must be expected outside the natural breeding season. Nevertheless, with all the difficulties, we have found that we now get better results, with healthier and younger breeding ewes, by running this small operation ourselves than by purchasing the culls from large flocks, or by trying to make arrangements with commercial breeders.

REFERENCES

Ciba Foundation Symposium (1969). *Foetal autonomy,* Churchill, London.

Ciba Foundation Symposium 27 (1974). *Size at birth,* Elsevier, Amsterdam.

Ciba Foundation Symposium 83 (1981a). *Development of the autonomic nervous system,* Elsevier, Amsterdam.

Ciba Foundation Symposium 86 (1981b). *The fetus and independent life,* Elsevier, Amsterdam.

Barcroft, J. (1947). *Researches on prenatal life*. Blackwells Scientific Publications, Oxford.

Elvidge, H. (1972). *J. Inst. Animal Tech.* **23**, 111–117.

Thurber, H. & Weeks, E. (1981). *Selected letters of James Thurber,* Hamish Hamilton, London.

7

The Chairman's summing-up

F. J. C. Roe DM(Oxon), DSc(Lond), FRC Path, Consultant in Toxicology and Adviser in Experimental Pathology & Cancer Research, 19 Marryat Road, London SW19 5BB

Broadly, I feel that we nowadays do have the knowledge and the means to produce essentially disease-free animals for research. Admittedly not all animal suppliers maintain the same high standards of our hosts today, and those who normally achieve high standards occasionally fall temporarily from grace. Nevertheless, we have during the past ten to fifteen years moved from the position where scientists engaged in biologically precise work were trying to persuade and educate animal suppliers to provide clean animals, to a position where educated animal suppliers are trying to persuade recalcitrant conservative animal users that the quality of their research would be greatly improved if they not only started their experiments with clean animals but also invested in facilities that enabled them to maintain animals under clean conditions in which they remain in good health. Personally, I believe that the use, in 1981, of randomly diseased and parasitised animals for any form of research is scientifically indefensible.

On the other hand, I have reservations about the advantages of inbred over random-bred animals for some kinds of experiment. If the animal is being used as a substitute for a test tube in order to measure some kind of biological activity for which there is presently no chemical or physical test, then obviously, inbred animals offer advantages: fewer are needed, variation in response is less, and confidence limits are narrower. But where the results of animal studies are to be extrapolated to man, inbred animals may give wholly misleading results. Some of the characteristics of inbred strains that have been deliberately or accidentally bred into them have little or no general human counterpart. Furthermore, I am suspicious that certain viral diseases have flourished because of inbreeding. I believe that Dr Rutty shares some of my doubts in this regard.

With the cleaning-up of laboratory animals, we have been able to see clearly for the first time problems that have probably been there all the time. In addition, as Mr Sebesteny pointed out, we have, during the cleaning-up process, introduced new problems. In this connection he mentioned the examples of vitamin K deficiency and vitamin E deficiency which occurred because these vitamins were destroyed during the pasteurisation of diets. I would add to this list the problems that we are now seeing because too much fat is added to diets. Without any thought of the nutritional consequences, the proportion of fat has been increased because a high fat content helps to prevent a pelleted diet from crumbling on exposure to steam used for sterilising purposes. Table 1, taken from Gellatly (1975), illustrates one disastrous effect of doubling the concentration of fat in a semisynthetic (SS) diet.

Table 1 – Incidence of liver tumours in $C_{57}BL$ female mice fed on a semisynthetic diet (SS) containing 5% or 10% ground nut oil (GNO).

	Mice with liver tumours (%) Benign or malignant	Malignant
SS diet with 5% GNO	8	1
SS diet with 10% GNO	43	9

From Gellatly (1975).

Dr Turnbull emphasised that he wants to know from animal suppliers precisely what animals have been fed on before they arrive at his laboratory. He is quite right to want to know this because nutrition during the early days of life can have profound effects on the subsequent growth and health of animals. Dr Rutty said a few things about the effects of dietary restriction on tumour incidence. I will, if I may, extend what he said.

Nutritionists are in general obsessed by the spectre of deficiency disease, but give much less thought to the consequences of over-nutrition. Their concept of the best diet is one that achieves the most rapid growth most efficiently during the first period of an animal's

life. By comparison, they have given little thought to the diseases of
overnutrition, and no one has warned the average experimentalist
involved in long-term studies that if he goes on feeding unlimited
amounts of unsuitably rich diets to animals throughout their lives they
will unnecessarily develop a whole galaxy of diseases which will interfere with the results of experiments and render their interpretation
difficult.

When animal colonies were cleaned-up many sources of stress
were removed from the environment of the animal laboratory. I think
that this stress, as undesirable as it was in other ways, served to
protect animals from the effects of overnutrition. Our pathogen-free
animals today lack exercise, lack sexual fulfilment (despite sitimula-
tion by the smell of the opposite sex often housed in the same room),
are provided *ad libitum* with unsuitably rich diets, and lack any form
of stress at all. In addition they now live long enough for us to see
in clear relief the evil effects of the artificiality of the conditions in
which we keep them.

It is my strongly held view that there is an urgent need for us to
reconsider the nutritional and social requirements of small laboratory
animals particularly during long-term experimentation.

Table 2 summarises tumour incidence data for untreated control
Sprague Dawley rats as reported by Kociba *et al.* (1979). Is it reasonable to accept, for example, a 63% incidence of pituitary tumours

**Table 2 – Hormone-associated neoplasms (%) in *ad libitum* fed
untreated control Sprague Dawley rats observed for up to 26 months
(86 rats of each sex).**

		♂	♀
Pituitary		31	63
Adrenal	— cortex	2	7
	medulla	51	8
Thyroid	— C-cell	8	8
Parathyroid		0	1
Pancreas	— exocrine	33	0
	endocrine	16	9
Testis		7	—
Ovary		—	5
Mammary	— fibroadenoma		76
gland	adenoma	5	12
	other		29

From Kociba *et al.* (1979).

and a more than 80% incidence of different kinds of mammary tumours in females, or a 51% incidence of adrenal medullary tumours and a 33% incidence of exocrine tumours of the pancreas in males as a suitable background for conducting a meaningful carcinogenicity study?

It is notable that most of these high-incidence tumours are of endocrine glands or sex hormone-controlled tissues. This, along with the fact that elderly control animals exhibit high incidences of non-neoplastic changes in the same tissues indicates that they are in severe disarray with regard to hormonal status.

Elsewhere (Roe 1981) I have pointed out that part of this disarray, but only part of it, can be rectified by simple and non-severe dietary restriction. By comparison with *ad libitum*-fed animals, diet-restricted animals are less obese, more active, and sleeker. Furthermore they live longer, and despite this their lifelong expectation of tumour development is significantly reduced. Surprisingly this reduction is not confined to tumours of kinds that are clearly linked to hormonal status. Table 3, taken from Tucker (1979), illustrates the dramatic effects of diet restriction in relation to pituitary and mammary tumours in rats, and Table 4, taken from Conybeare (1980), does so for a variety of tumours including liver, lung, and lymphoreticular neoplasms in mice.

There is growing evidence that the effects of dietary restriction are not solely attributable to reduction in calorie intake. The mere fact of an animal being faced for a part of each day by an empty food basket seems to be important. In the absence of a visible source of food, plasma cortico-steroid levels rise and it is perhaps the regular occurrence of this that protects animals from the ravages of progressive hormonal disarray. One marker of such increasing disarray in rats is the pattern of pathologically high and rising serum prolactin levels with age from about the sixth month of life onwards (Table 5).

I suggest, then, that one of the biggest challenges for the future is to devise ways of maintaining untreated laboratory animals in normal hormonal status throughout their lives. Until we do this it is unreasonable to regard them as models for the study of age-related disease in humankind, or as suitable for the testing of chemical agents for carcinogenicity. I hope that this can be an area in which the researchminded animal breeder as well as the nutritionist can play a big role, but the real breakthrough may come only when we have available methods for monitoring the hormonal status of individual living rats and mice — that is to say micro-methods that entail the analysis of only very small samples of blood. When we have these methods, then it will be possible to investigate the influence of the

Table 3 – Effect of dietary restriction on incidence of pituitary and mammary tumours in rats

Feeding regimen	Males		Females	
	Ad lib.	Restricted	*Ad lib.*	Restricted
Rats with pituitary tumours (%)	32	0***	66	39**
Rats with mammary tumours (%)	0	0	34	6***

**P < 0.01, ***P < 0.001.
From Tucker (1979).

Table 4 – Effect of simple dietary restriction on tumour incidence in mice. Number of mice which developed tumours at any time during the study. There were 160 mice of each sex in each group.

Feeding regimen	Males		Females	
		Restricted to		Restricted to
	Ad lib.	75% of *ad lib.*	*Ad lib.*	75% of *ad lib.*
Type of tumour				
Lung	30	19*	24	8**
Liver	47	12***	7	1*
Lymphoma	4	1	11	4*
Other	8	4	12	4*
Any tumour at any site	71	36***	50	17**
Any malignant tumour	17	7*	23	7**

*P < 0.05, **P < 0.01, ***P < 0.001.
From Conybeare (1980).

Table 5 – Serum prolactin levels in *ad libitum*-fed Sprague-Dawley rats.

Age (months)	ng/ml	
	0	0
2	26	21
3	27	37
4	28	34
7	35	74
13	128	214
19	119	345

N.B. Level in non-pregnant women = 20 – 40 ng/ml.

unnatural aspects of the life of caged laboratory animals listed in Table 6.

Table 6 — Unnatural aspects of the life of a control rat.

1. Food available 24 hours per day
2. Excessively nutritious diet
3. No need to forage
4. Doesn't have to avoid predators
5. Enforced celibacy despite sexual stimulation
6. General boredom

REFERENCES

Conybeare, G. (1980) *Fd. Cosmet. Toxicol.* **18**, 65.

Gellatly, J. B. (1975) In *Hepatic neoplasia*, Butler, W. H. & Newberne, P. M. Eds., p.77, Elsevier Scientific, Amsterdam.

Kociba, R. J., Keyes, D. G., Lisowe, R. W. Kalnins, R. P., Dittenber, D. D., Wade, C. E., Gorzinski, S. J., Mahle, N. H. & Schwetz, B. A. (1979) *Fd. Cosmet. Toxicol.* **17**, 205–221.

Roe, F. J. C. (1981) *Proc. Nutr. Soc.* **40**, 57–65.

Tucker, M. J. (1979) *Int. J. Cancer* **23**, 803.

8

Quality control procedures followed by Bantin & Kingman

G. Bulfield BSc, PhD, A. A. Deeny BSc, and J. D. Kelly BSc, BVM&S, MRCVS, Bantin & Kingman Ltd., The Field Station, Grimston, Aldebrough, Hull, HU11 4QE.

INTRODUCTION

The ultimate role of animals produced by a breeder is to serve as a tool in biomedical research. Therefore, the aim of this symposium has been to establish the requirements of the scientist for a defined animal in terms of its health status, genetic authenticity, and environment, prior to use.

Awareness of the need for both suppliers and users to define laboratory animals in such a way has been increased over the years by the MRC Accreditation Scheme. However, this scheme has not been of a sufficient scale or sufficiently comprehensive in its coverage to meet the more sophisticated needs of users in more recent years. The principle, however, is now firmly founded, and the advanced animal breeder must look to building on this basis to achieve a workable and meaningful quality control programme.

It is interesting to note that all the speakers at the symposium come out strongly in favour of microbiological screening. Micro-organisms can interfere with the immune system, in experimental systems for oncogenic studies, in toxicological and pathological examinations, and in the academic study of the microorganisms themselves. Several speakers have made reference not only to pathogenic organisms, but to the need to define more closely the normal flora. Other factors that appear to be of great importance are correct nutrition and feeding patterns, provision of an environment which is consistent with that of future experimental accommodation, and minimisation of stress by providing suitable means of transport.

Several aspects should be considered when choosing an animal as an experimental model. The experimental protocol should indicate the animal best suited to the experiment, and unless the quality of the animal is high, reliability of the data generated may be compromised in studies requiring long-term holding. Since the cost in time and money may be great, safeguards must be instituted to protect the experiment. Knowledge that options are available permits the rational selection by genetic history, microbiological status, breeder source, environment, and method of transportation. It is useful, therefore, to outline the protocols of microbiological screening at Bantin & Kingman in response to some of the salient questions raised at the symposium.

It has to be accepted that the state of health of any animal colony is at permanent risk of undesirable infection. Since infection is not synonymous with disease, it must also be accepted that initially at least, many infections may be inapparent, or at least not manifest in the form of grossly obvious lesions. Indeed, since some infections produce disease only when the animals are stressed in some way, apparently healthy but infected animals may leave the breeding unit and break down when subjected to experiment. Therefore, it is generally accepted that microbiological screening of laboratory animals plays an important role in maintaining healthy stock.

We are aware that a primary consideration in long-term studies is the maintenance of animals under conditions that prevent the introduction of unwanted organisms and provide a high degree of microbial stability throughout the life-span. Whilst it is clear to most investigators that an epizootic that destroys an ongoing experiment represents a serious hazard, the more subtle effects of latent microbial infections are less widely understood. Therefore, we have invested heavily in the further development of the flexible film isolator, which provides a practical means to isolate an animal completely from environmental biological contaminants. We have found these to be most useful in the housing of animals of known microbial status. By constant monitoring of the isolator and the animals housed therein we can be assured that the condition of the animals will remain in a steady state for an indefinite period.

Laboratory animals have played a major part in our growing understanding of biological processes. Their past contributions have been the basis for many of our current explorations into new and more sophisticated areas of investigation, but as the questions asked become more fundamental, and the techniques used more precise, the adequacy of the animal must be proved. More investigators and animal producers have become aware that high-quality animals, genetically, microbiologically, and environmentally defined, are essential for certain types of experiment. Isolator-reared animals are now seen with increasing frequency at many institutions and commercial breeding establishments, as many investigators are learning that subtle as well as obvious changes in microbial, chemical, or physical factors can significantly influence the generation and interpretation of experimental data.

As the state of the art of laboratory animal medicine improves, new methods will solve old problems. However, awareness of the criteria as recognised by current practitioners of the art will improve the final chance of success in experiments requiring the use of laboratory animals.

SCREENING PROCEDURES IN USE AT BANTIN & KINGMAN

In using a normal barrier-maintained animal, there is already a degree of microbiological variance within the colony, and such variance, if undesirable to the user, can best be deleted by using a gnotobiotic animal. (Coates, 1975; Trexler & Reynolds, 1957). However, in the absence of such a high-grade animal, especially in experiments or tests requiring routine operations on large nunbers of animals, it is obviously of great importance for the breeder and user to be assured that the animals they are housing are free from the important pathogenes. A simple method of making the screen positive is to use the methods employed in screening out these pathogens (AMAC, 1972) and subsequently to identify *all* the organisms cultured (Table 1).

A parasitological examination is most important, though it is only fairly recently that the effects of parasites on the hosts' systems has been identified to any extent (Table 2). Many of these effects have been well-documented in the paper given by Dr Worms.

The common wild rodent carries a considerable parasite burden. Many of these parasites are of importance to the research worker who uses rodents. Although comparatively few of the forms have much influence on the wellbeing of the animal in the natural state, under laboratory conditions, and especially under experimental conditions, they may develop into serious factors, not only because of their deleterious effects on the animal, but also because they may act as an experimental variable (Keast & Chesterman, 1972; Boorman *et al.* 1973).

The extent of viral screening has, in the past, been fairly limited. Spontaneous diseases due to viruses have been recognised for some time, though the mouse appears to be susceptible to many more than

Table 1 — Screening methodology — bacteriology.

Site of culture	Media	Incubating conditions	Pathogens excluded
Nasopharynx	Blood agar	Aerobic at 37°C (24–48 hours)	*Bordetella bronchiseptica*
			Pasteurella spp.
			Streptococcus GpA
			Corynebacterium spp.
			Listeria monocytogenes
			Yersinia pseudotuberculosis
	30% serum agar	Aerobic + 10% CO₂ at 37°C (24–48 hours)	*Streptococcus pneumoniae*
	PPLO agar	Aerobic at 37°C in humid atmosphere (24–48 hours)	*Streptobacillus moniliformis*
	PPLO broth	95% N2 + 5% CO₂ at 37°C (not less than 3 weeks)	*Mycoplasma* spp.
		Aerobic at 37°C (6 weeks)	
Trachea	Nutrient broth then	Aerobic at 37°C (24 hours)	
	Blood agar	Aerobic at 37°C (24 hours)	*Bordetella bronchiseptica*
Caecum	Selenite broth then	Aerobic at 37°C (24–48 hours)	*Salmonella* spp.
	Desoxycholate citrate agar		
	Bismuth sulphite agar	Aerobic at 37°C (24–48 hours)	
	Blood agar	Aerobic at 37°C (24–48 hours)	*Yersinia* spp.
			Listeria monocytogenes
Additional tests:			
Lung	Blood agar	Aerobic at 37°C (24–48 hours)	General use
Caecum	MacConkey agar	Aerobic at 37°C (24–48 hours)	General use

Table 2 – Screening methodology – parasitology.

Site	Examination	Parasites sought
Pelt	Examination behind neck and ears, around eyes and nose	Ectoparasites and their eggs
Small intestine	Wet preparations of contents of inner lining of the wall	Flagellates and other protozoa
Large intestine	Wet preparations of contents	Nematodes, protozoan cysts, protozoa, and other parasites
Faeces	Flotation and/or wet preparations	Eggs, oocysts, and cysts
Blood	Thin films stained with Giemsa	Haemoflagellates and other protozoa

the rat. Virus infections can seriously interfere with research work (Baker *et al.* 1979) therefore, the screen adopted by Bantin & Kingman is, through necessity, extensive (Table 3).

Table 3 – Viruses screened – carried out by Microbiological Associates Inc.

Virus	Rats	Mice	Guinea-pigs
Sendai	●	●	●
Mouse hepatitis		●	
Lymphocytic choriomeningitis	●	●	●
Ectromelia		●	
Kilham rat virus	●		
Polyoma virus		●	
Reovirus type 3		●	
Mouse adenovirus		●	
SDAV/RCV	●		

Many laboratories pay little or no attention to the size of sample taken for monitoring. It is difficult in these circumstances to be even reasonably certain that the organisms sought would be detected unless the size of the sample is statistically significant. Therefore Bantin & Kingman can supply the following information:
(a) actual sample size per month;
(b) percentage of the colony the sample represents;
(c) age and sex of the animals sampled.

The sample size is calculated from the equation

$$S = \frac{\log 0.05}{\log N}$$

where S = sample size, N = percentage of normal animals (Ilar, 1976).

The prevalence rate is $(100-N)$. Thus this equation predicts the sample size required to detect a single case of the disease of prevalence rate $(100-N)$ in a population of 100 animals to within 95% confidence limits.

This standard equation, designed for the detection of single diseases, has been adapted to monitor a range of organisms within the screening programme. The organisms excluded by this programme are:

Bordetella, Corynebacterium, Listeria, Mycobacteria, Mycoplasma, Pasteurella, Pneumococcus, Salmonella, Streptobacillus, Streptococcus GpA, Yersinia.

The prevalence rates of diseases caused by these organisms in a laboratory animal colony range from 11–90%. The lowest prevalence rate has been taken as the point of reference, and the sample size based on that rate.

Therefore in a breeding unit of, for example, 2000 animals the sample size is calculated as

$$S = \frac{\log 0.05}{\log 0.89} \times 20 = 514.$$

This number is made manageable by denoting S as the sample size per annum. Therefore, the number sampled in any six-week period is 60.

In large animal units it is acceptable to take into account the average caging density and the number of cages in each animal unit. In this way, one cage is taken to represent one animal. For example, if in the colony described above the animals were housed 10 per cage, the sample size $S = 52$ and the six-weekly sample would therefore be 6. Such a sample size is manageable for both the animal unit and the laboratory. The annual percentage of the total colonly that the sample represents is 2.6% in all cases using this system, and the six-weekly percentage is 0.3%.

The sample includes a range of ages from weanlings to ex-breeders, and an equal number of either sex. Furthermore, the sampling from within the unit is randomised to preclude repeatedly screening animals from the same area.

THE NEED FOR GENETIC MONITORING

The use of inbred strains (especially of the laboratory mouse) in biochemical research has exploded over the last twenty years. In areas such as pharmacology and cancer research the use of inbred strains provides animals that are identical to each other, therefore removing the genetic component of biological variability. It is just because of the reliance placed on the uniformity and repeatability of inbred animals that it is essential to ensure that they do not change genetically in time and place.

In principle this seems a formidable task because substrains of an inbred strain (such as the mouse strain C57BL/6) are distributed all over the world with each scientist requiring reproducibility both with his own previous results and those of others in other laboratories and countries using the same strain. This wide distribution of inbred strains exposes them to substrain divergence or contamination with other strains.

The extent of substrain divergence is not easy to assess. Early attempts to measure the extent of divergence using morphological characteristics, showed that the C57BL strain, imported to Britain in the 1930s, had diverged considerably 25 years later (Deol *et al.* 1957, Hoi-Sen 1971. See also: Morse 1979). Similarly Groen (1977) found widespread substrain divergence among 53 inbred strains from three Dutch institutes using biochemical polymorphisms.

The work of Groen points to another problem, that of strain contamination. Several of the Dutch inbred strains were segregating at different loci; one at four loci. This indicates that they have been contaminated recently. In fact, because of the breeding structure of inbred strains, only recent contamination will show as segregating alleles at a locus. Alleles introduced by less recent contamination can be removed (or fixed), thus apparently minimising substrain divergence. It is interesting to note that substrains kept under almost ideal conditions by the Jackson Laboratory (Taylor 1972, Altman & Katz 1979; Morse 1979) exhibit little substrain divergence in bio-chemical polymorphisms or at histocomparatibility loci. For example the mouse inbred strains C57BL/6 and C57BL/10 (separated since 1932: about 120 generations) differ at only two out of over 60 loci examined (Altman & Katz 1979).

Therefore when we examine discrete characteristics (whose genetic basis is understood) we find that allelic differences between substrains are more likely to be due to contamination than to new mutations. This means that we are in a position to prevent these differences between substrains, either through time or in different locations, by genetic monitoring for contamination.

GENETIC MONITORING TECHNIQUES

There is a range of genetic monitoring techniques available to us (Review: Festing 1979). They are discussed briefly below.

(a) *Coat colour*

Several inbred strains of mice and rats have unusual coat colour genes. For example, the dilute-brown-nonagouti phenotype of the DBA/2 strain or the white head-spot of the F/St strain. In a relatively small breeding colony even the agouti of C3H or the black of C57BL can be a useful strain marker. More usually coat colour markers are of limited use; the main problem is that so many strains of rats and mice are albino. The simple rule is to keep strains of the same coat colour physically apart.

(b) *Histocompatability testing*

The commonest way of testing for identity at histocompatability loci is by skin grafting (see Festing 1979). This procedure can be used for inbred strains of rats, mice, guinea-pigs, and rabbits, and is quite sensitive because rejection or acceptance of the graft is controlled by loci that are very variable against laboratory animals. It is, however, open to operator error and other environmental variables, and the results are not always as objective as might be desired.

A new method for histocompatability monitoring has recently been developed using polyvalent strain-specific alloantisera (Festing & Totman 1980) which may prove to be simpler, more sensitive, and more objective than skin grafting.

(c) *Skeletal morphology*

As mentioned earlier, there are significant morphological differences between strains and substrains of laboratory rodents (and probably other species). These skeletal differences are polygenic, being controlled by several to many genes. This is an advantage in that it makes the character sensitive to contamination or mutation. It is also a disadvantage in that it is not possible to assess how many allelic differences are responsible for a morphological variation caused by contamination or divergence, i.e. how serious the problem is. There is also the complication that morphological characters have already been shown to change in a remarkably few generations (0.01 changes per character per generation; Hoi-Sen 1972), a rate of instability incompatible with the known mutation rate, and they also show epigenetic (spontaneous developmental) modification.

A system of genetic monitoring using eleven measurements of mandible shape has been developed for the MRC Laboratory

Animals Centre by Festing. This technique has been in use success-
fully for several years, monitoring the inbred mice and rats produced
by accredited breeders in the UK (Review: Festing 1979). The
system depends on building up a bank of data centrally on baseline
parameters for each strain, then using discriminate functions and
statistical goodness-of-fit tests to ascertain whether a substrain is
contaminated or not.

(d) *Biochemical polymorphisms*

Alleles at loci coding for proteins affect the amino acid composition
of the protein and can alter its 'charge'. These 'biochemical polymorphisms' can be detected by various forms of gel electrophoresis
or electrofocusing as a qualitative difference in the position of the
enzyme or other protein in the gel. It is therefore possible to say
exactly which allele a particular strain or substrain possesses.

As the products of well over fifty loci in the mouse can be
detected by these procedures, a battery of electrophoretic analyses
could, in principle, distinguish unequivocally one strain from another,
or investigate a strain for contamination with any other strain. A
battery of these tests requires technical expertise not at present available to most suppliers of laboratory animals. In practice, however,
most laboratories require to monitor a restricted number of inbred
strains for evidence of cross-contamination (especially between albino
strains). In such cases it is easy to devise a few simple electrophoretic
systems to distinguish the strains unequivocally from each other.

We have extended the use of biochemical polymorphisms by the
determination of phenotypes on a blood sample from a live animal
for the *Hba, Hbb,* and *Gpi*-1 loci all on one electrofocusing gel
(Fig. 1: Bulfield and Bantin 1981). This enables us to distinguish most
of the strains held by Bantin and Kingman. There are, however, two
disadvantages. One lies in typing the commonly used A, AKR and
BALB/c group of albino strains. These do differ at the *Hba* locus
(Fig. 1) and can often be distinguished but not unequivocally. The
electrofocusing is therefore backed up with *Pep*-3 typing which will
separate BALB/c from AKR and A; to distinguish AKR from A and
BALB/c the animal has to be typed for *Idh*-1 (Fig. 1). The other disadvantage is in separating substrains C57BL/6 and C57BL/10 from
each other (differing at only two out of over 60 loci) and separating
congenic strains. The latter are mainly congenic for the H-2 complex,
and can be separated only by immunological techniques. The electrofocusing procedure (Bulfield & Bantin 1981) will, however, monitor
substrains from all strains other than their cohorts, and therefore in
practice this might not be a serious disadvantage.

Strain: Locus	A	AKR	BALB/c	CBA	C57BL/ 10	CE	C3H	DBA/2	SJL	SWR
Hba/ Hbb	=	=	=	—	—	—	≡	=	=	=
Gpi-1	—	—	—	—	—	—	—	—	—	—
Idh-1	—	—	—	—	—	—	—	—	—	—
Pep-3	—	—	—	—	—	—	—	—	—	—

Fig. 8.1 – Diagrammatic representation of gel patterns of enzymes in inbred strains of mice; each strain can be unambiguously distinguished from all others.

This procedure has been in operation for 4 years (each six months each strain is sampled) and has proved satisfactory in confirming that the strains are in accordance with the phenotypes from the literature (Taylor 1972, Altman & Katz 1979). From time to time over this period colonies from other laboratories have been sampled where contamination was suspected. When contamination had occurred it was obvious and was picked up in several animals in the stock and often at more than one locus. We are, therefore, satisfied that electrofocusing will determine whether any of the inbred strains become contaminated.

With random-bred strains the problem is more difficult as the frequency of alleles will be expected to drift with time and from laboratory to laboratory. One attempt has, however, been made to use biochemical polymorphisms to monitor random-bred mice within one Institute (Groen & Lagerwerf 1979).

The use of biochemical polymorphisms as a basis for genetic monitoring of inbred strains of rats (and rabbits) is hampered by the lack of information on variation at the common isoenzyme loci (Altman & Katz 1979). For example, the common inbred strains of rats do not show differences at the *Hba* and *Hbb* loci by electrofocusing (Bulfield, unpublished observations). Therefore at the moment, until we have more information on biochemical polymorphisms, other techniques of genetic monitoring will have to be used.

It can be concluded that where a restricted number of mouse inbred strains have to be monitored for genetic contamination a simple electrofocusing/electrophoresis system can be established which can authenticate the strains in a qualitative and unequivocal manner.

REFERENCES

Accreditation Microbiological Advisory Committee (1972). *Microbiological Examination of Laboratory Animals for the Purposes of Accreditation*. M. R. C. Labatory Animals Centre.

Altman, P. L. & Katz, D. D. (eds) (1974). *Inbred and Genetically Defined Strains of Laboratory Animals. Part 1. Mouse and Rat.* Bethesda: Federation of American Societies for Experimental Biology.

Baker, H. J., Lindsay, J. R. & Weisbroth, S. H. (eds) (1979). *The Laboratory Rat. Volume 1. Biology and Diseases*. Academic Press, New York & London.

Boorman, G. A., van Hooft, J. I., van der Waaij, D. & van Noord, M. J. (1973). Synergistic role of intestinal flagellates and normal intestinal bacteria in a post-weaning mortality of mice. *Laboratory Animal Science* **23**, 187.

Bulfield, G. & Bantin, G. (1981). Genetic monitoring of inbred strains using electrophoresis and electrofocusing. *Laboratory Animals* **15**, 147–149.

Coates, M. E. (1975). Gnotobiotic animals in research: their uses and limitations. *Laboratory Animals* **9**, 275.

Deol, M. S., Gruneberg, H., Searle, A. G. & Truelove, G. M. (1957). Genetic differentiation involving morphological characters in an inbred strain of mice. 1. A British branch of the $C_{57}BL$ strain. *Journal of Morphology* **100**, 345–376.

Festing, M. F. W. (1979). *Inbred Strains in Biomedical Research*. Macmillan, London.

Festing, M. F. W. & Totman, P. (1980). Polyvalent strain – specific allowances as tools for routine genetic quality control of inbred and congenic strains of rats and mice. *Laboratory Animals* **14**, 173–177.

Groen, A. (1977). Identification and genetic monitoring of mouse inbred strains using biochemical polymorphisms. *Laboratory Animals* **11**, 209–214.

Groen, A. & Lagerwerf, A. J. (1979). Genic heterogeneity and genetic monitoring of mouse inbred stocks. *Laboratory Animals* **13**, 81–85.

Hoi-Sen, Y. (1972). Is subline differentiation a continuing process in inbred strains of mice. *Genetical Research* **19**, 53–59.

Institute of Laboratory Animal Resources (1976). *A Report of the Committee on Long Term Holding of Laboratory Rodents.* Assembly of Life Sciences: National Research Council.

Keast, D. & Chesterman, F. C. (1972). Changes in macrophage metabolism in mice heavily infected with *Hexamita muris. Laboratory Animals* **6**, 33.

Morse, H. C. (ed.) (1979). *Origins of Inbred Mice.* Academic Press, London.

Taylor, B. A. (1972). Genetic relationships between inbred strains of mice. *Journal of Heredity* **63**, 83–86.

Trexler, P. C. & Reynolds, L. I. (1957). Flexible film appratus for the rearing and use of germ-free animals. *Applied Microbiology* **5**, 406.

Index